The Tools of Owatatsumi
Japan's Ocean Surveillance and Coastal Defence Capabilities

The Tools of Owatatsumi
Japan's Ocean Surveillance and Coastal Defence Capabilities

Desmond Ball and Richard Tanter

PRESS

Published by ANU Press
The Australian National University
Canberra ACT 0200, Australia
Email: anuepress@anu.edu.au
This title is also available online at http://press.anu.edu.au

National Library of Australia Cataloguing-in-Publication entry

Title: The tools of Owatatsumi : Japan's ocean surveillance and coastal defence
                 capabilities / Desmond Ball, Richard Tanter.

ISBN: 9781925022261 (paperback) 9781925022278 (ebook)

Subjects: Boundary disputes.
                 Underwater surveillance--Japan.
                 Coast defenses--Japan.
                 Territorial waters--Japan.
                 Territorial waters--China.
                 United States--Foreign relations--Japan
                 Japan--Foreign relations--United States.

Other Authors/Contributors:
                 Tanter, Richard, author.

Dewey Number: 327.14

Cover design and layout by ANU Press

Printed by Griffin Press

This edition © 2015 ANU Press

Contents

Frontispiece

Katsushika Hokusai, Dragon

Japan's creation mythology, as recorded in the eighth century Kojiki and Nihongi chronicles, depicts Owatatsumi (大綿津見) as the first god born of the country's founding brother and sister, Izanagi and Izanami. Owatatsumi is the lord god of the sea, sometimes called Ryjujin or dragon god (龍神). Master of the sea and its denizens, Owatatsumi appears in the shape of a dragon.

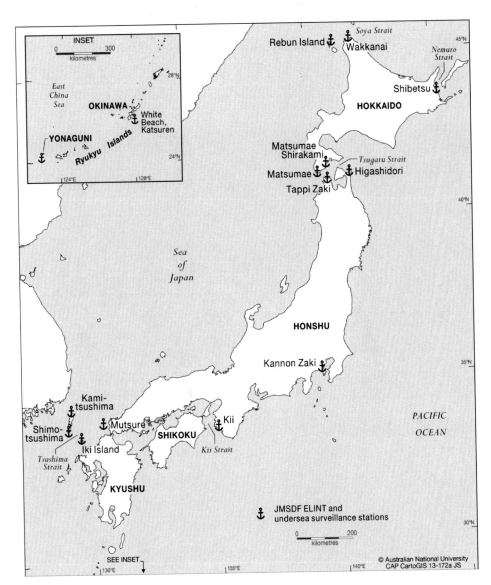

Map 1. JMSDF ELINT and undersea surveillance stations

Source: ANU CAP CartoGIS

Plates

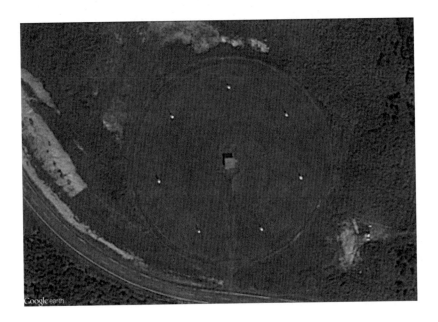

Plate 1. JGSDF Coastal Surveillance Unit 301, Wakkanai, (7-element CDAA for HF/VHF interception and DF), 16 August 2010

Source: Imagery © Google, DigitalGlobe, dated 16 August 2010

Plate 2. JGSDF Coastal Surveillance Unit 301, Maruyama, September 2011

Source: Desmond Ball Collection

Plate 3. JGSDF Coastal Surveillance Unit 301, Rebun, 7 September 2005

Source: Desmond Ball Collection

**Plate 4. JGSDF Coastal Surveillance Unit 302, Shibetsu (Inset: Kawakita),
7 September 2011**

Source: Desmond Ball Collection

Plate 5. Detachment of the JGSDF 302 Coastal Surveillance Unit, Rausu, Hokkaido, 10 September 2005

Source: Desmond Ball Collection

Plate 6. JGSDF Coastal Surveillance Unit 302, radome and antenna towers at Nemuro, 7 September 2011

Source: Desmond Ball Collection

Plate 7. JGSDF Coastal Surveillance Unit 302, Nemuro, (7-element CDAA for HF/VHF interception and DF), 3 September 2010

Source: Imagery © Google, DigitalGlobe, dated 3 September 2010

Plate 8. JMSDF Coastal Surveillance Station, Notsuke Peninsula, Shibetsu, Hokkaido, 6 September 2011

Source: Desmond Ball Collection

Plate 9. JMSDF ELINT/undersea surveillance station, Matsumae Shirakami, 11 September 2011

Source: Desmond Ball Collection

Plate 10. JMSDF Coastal Defence Station, Matsumae, 11 September 2011

Source: Desmond Ball Collection

Plate 11. JMSDF ELINT/undersea surveillance station, Tappi Zaki, 20 August 1982

Source: Desmond Ball Collection

Plate 12. JMSDF ELINT/undersea surveillance station, Kii, 2008

Source: Desmond Ball Collection

Plate 13. JMSDF ELINT/undersea surveillance station, Kii, 16 August 2006

Source: Kim Keukmi

Plate 14. JMSDF ESM radome at Kii, 16 August 2006

Source: Kim Keukmi

Plate 15. JMSDF ELINT station, Mutsure-jima, 7 October 2010

Source: Desmond Ball Collection

Plate 16. JMSDF ELINT station, Mutsure-jima, 7 October 2010

Source: Desmond Ball Collection

Plate 17. JMSDF ELINT station, Oura, Kami-tsushima, Tushima Islands, 17 February 2010

Source: Desmond Ball Collection

Plate 18. JMSDF ELINT station, Agami, Shimo-tsushima, 16 February 2010

Source: Desmond Ball Collection

Plate 19. JMSDF ELINT station, Agami, Shimo-tsushima, 16 February 2010

Source: Desmond Ball Collection

Plate 20. JMSDF ESM system, Tsutsu, Shimo-tsushima, Tushima Islands, 18 February 2010

Source: Desmond Ball Collection

Plate 21. JMSDF ELINT station, Wakamiya, Iki Island

Source: Desmond Ball Collection

Plate 22. JMSDF Coastal Defense Station, Kogozaki, Sasebo, 16 March 2012

Source: Desmond Ball Collection

Plate 23. JCG 7-element HF DF station, Ishigaki, 4 July 2010

Source: Imagery © Google, DigitalGlobe, dated 4 July 2010

Plate 24. JCG 7-element HF DF station, Ishigaki, December 2013

Source: Desmond Ball Collection

Acknowledgements

The authors are very grateful to several friends and colleagues who assisted us with this project. Our interest in Japan's signals intelligence (SIGINT) capabilities and activities was in large part inspired by Sato Yuji and Owen Wilkes, two peace researchers who, in the 1980s, comprehensively and systematically studied all of Japan's major SIGINT facilities, as well as many US SIGINT facilities in Japan. Both are now long dead, but we have been fortunate to inherit copies of most of the material they collected. Jeffrey T. Richelson, who published the first account of the Japanese Maritime Self-Defence Force's undersea surveillance stations in English in 1988, generously gave us copies of much relevant material. Kim Keukmi and Leon K. White provided us with wonderful research support. Bill Robinson has been unsparing in his assistance, making his holdings of satellite imagery available to us, and calculating the dimensions of many of the antenna elements described herein.

Desmond Ball also wishes to thank his wife, Annabel Rossiter, and his children Katie, Matthew and James, for their love and forbearance. Richard Tanter would like to thank Luisa Macmillan and Kai and Nathaniel Tanter for their love and support through those long absences in mind and body.

Acronyms and Abbreviations

ADEOS	Advanced Earth Observing Satellite
ADIZ	Air Defence Identification Zone
AESA	active electronically scanned array
AGI	Auxiliary General Intelligence ship
ASW	anti-submarine warfare
BIC	Basic Intelligence Center
CAFS	Chinese Academy of Fisheries Sciences
CDAA	circularly disposed antenna array
COMINT	communications intelligence
COTS	commercial off-the-shelf
DF	direction-finding
DIFAR	directional acoustic frequency analysis and recording
DIH	Defense Intelligence Headquarters
DGPS	Differential Global Positioning System
DPS	dynamic positioning system
DSCS	US Defense Satellite Communications System
ECM	electronic countermeasures
ECCM	electronic counter-countermeasures
EEZ	exclusive economic zone
EIC	Electronic Intelligence Center
ELINT	electronic intelligence
EOSU	Electronic Operations Support Unit
ESM	electronic support measures
EW	electronic warfare
FBG	Fibre Bragg Gratings
FIC	Fleet Intelligence Center/Command
FLIR	forward-looking infra-red
FOSIC	US Fleet Ocean Surveillance Information Center
FOSIF	US Fleet Ocean Surveillance Information Facility
FY	fiscal year
GMDSS	Global Maritime Distress and Safety System
HF	high frequency (3–30 megahertz)
HF DF	high frequency direction finding
HQ	headquarters

ICE	improved collection equipment
IJN	Imperial Japanese Navy
IOD	Information Operations Directorate
IRSS	infra-red suppression system
J-AOS	Japanese Auxiliary Oceanographic System
JASDF	Japanese Air Self-Defense Force
JASREP	Japanese Ship Reporting System
JCG	Japan Coast Guard
JDA	Japan Defense Agency
JGSDF	Japanese Ground Self-defense Force
JICPAC	US Joint Intelligence Center – Pacific
JMSDF	Japanese Maritime Self-Defense Force
JODC	Japan Oceanographic Data Center
JOED	JMSDF OSIS Evolutionary Development
JOSIS	JMSDF Ocean Surveillance Information System
JSDF	Japanese Self-Defense Force
LFA	low-frequency active
LPA	log-periodic array
LRMP	long-range maritime patrol
MAD	magnetic anomaly detection
MoD	Ministry of Defense
MESSR	Multispectral Electronic Self-Scanning Radiometer
MOS	Marine Observation Satellite
MSA	Maritime Safety Agency
MSO	Maritime Staff Office
MSR	Microwave Scanning Radiometer
MTDP	Mid-Term Defense Program
NETWARCOM	Naval Network Warfare Command
NCGA	Taiwanese National Coast Guard Administration
NIOC	Navy Information Operations Command
NIOD	Navy Information Operations Detachment
NOSIC	US Naval Ocean Surveillance Information Center
NOSS	US Naval Ocean Surveillance System
NSGA	US Naval Security Group Activity
OBU	OSIS Baseline Upgrade
OED	OBU Evolutionary Development
OIC	Operational Intelligence Center

OSIS	Ocean Surveillance Information System
PLA	People's Liberation Army
PLAN	People's Liberation Army Navy
PSI	Proliferation Security Initiative
RDA	reduced diameter array
ROV	remotely operated vehicle
Satcom	satellite communications
SHF	super high frequency (3–30 gigahertz)
SIGINT	signals intelligence
SLOC	sea-lines of communication
SOSUS	sound surveillance system
SSBL	super-short-base-line
SSN	nuclear-powered attack submarine
SST	sea surface temperature
SURTASS	Surveillance Towed Array Sensor System
TRDI	Technical Research and Development Institute
UAV	unmanned aerial vehicle
UHF	ultra high frequency (300 megahertz – 3 gigahertz)
US	United States
USAF	US Air Force
USPACOM	US Pacific Command
VHF	very high frequency (30–300 megahertz)
VTIR	Visible and Thermal Infra-red Radiometer

1. Introduction

Japan is quintessentially by geography a maritime country. It consists of four main islands (Hokkaido, Honshu, Shikoku and Kyushu), no part of which is more than 150 kilometres from the sea, and about 3,000 smaller islands (including Okinawa) and islets, some of which are uninhabited. Its claimed exclusive economic zone (EEZ) is 4.51 million square kilometres, compared to its total land territory of only 380,000 square kilometres. Its coastline is nearly 35,000 kilometres in length (the sixth longest in the world), or 91 metres for every square kilometre of land area.[1] Except for the northernmost island of Hokkaido, the interiors of the islands are 'mountainous, steep, and difficult to develop or farm', so that the population is concentrated along the coasts, and especially on a several 'spacious low-lying plains', typically centred around large natural harbours that have grown into 'huge urbanised ports', such as Tokyo, Kawasaki and Yokohama on the Kanto Plain, which comprise about a third of Japan's population; Osaka and Kobe, which together with Kyoto, form the Kansai District; and Nagoya on the Nobi Plain.[2] Its economy is vitally dependent on long and vulnerable sea-lines of communication (SLOC) for a very high proportion of its energy and raw materials requirements.[3]

A maritime country requires a maritime defence, and maritime capabilities were the centrepiece of Japanese rearmament, under the direction of the US Navy, which began in the early 1950s. Coastal defence groups were established immediately the National Safety Force was established by Yoshida Shigeru in April 1952, following the signing of the San Francisco Peace Treaty and the US–Japan Mutual Security Treaty in September 1951. These were initially an autonomous part of the Maritime Safety Agency (MSA), which was established on 1 May 1948 to perform constabulary and coastguard functions, but became part of the Maritime Safety Force, established on 1 August 1952, and reorganised into the Japanese Maritime Self-Defense Force (JMSDF) in July 1954.[4]

Since its formation, the JMSDF has incrementally but progressively and inexorably expanded its capabilities, roles and missions, increasing its 'sphere of activities [in] an ever widening circle'.[5] Through its first decade, its principal

---

1 'Geography of Japan', *Wikipedia*, at en.wikipedia.org/wiki/Geography_of_Japan; and Masahiko Isobe, 'A Theory of Integrated Coastal Zone Management in Japan', at www.glocom.ac.jp/eco/esena/resource/isobe/index.e.html
2 Peter J. Woolley, *Japan's Navy: Politics and Paradox, 1971–2000* (Lynne Rienner, Boulder, Colorado, 2000), p. 6.
3 Euan Graham, *Japan's Sea Lane Security, 1940–2004: A Matter of Life and Death?* (Routledge, London, 2006), chpt 1.
4 James E. Auer, *The Postwar Rearmament of Japanese Maritime Forces, 1945–71* (Praeger, New York, 1973), chpt 5.
5 Woolley, *Japan's Navy*, p. 24.

avowed focus was on defence of harbours and ports. In the mid-1960s, it graduated to defence of some of the narrower straits. The Third Defense Program (1967–71), approved by the Cabinet in November 1966, outlined the objective of 'increasing the ability to defend coastal areas, straits and surrounding waters'; it was intended to provide the JMSDF with the capability to monitor submarine traffic passing through the Soya (or La Perouse) Strait between Hokkaido and Sakhalin Island, through the Tsugaru Strait between Hokkaido and Honshu, and through the Tsushima Strait between Korea and Japan.[6] In January 1983, Prime Minister Yasuhiro Nakasone, a former director general of the Japan Defense Agency (JDA) (1970–72), declared that Japanese defence policy would ensure 'full control of four straits that go through the Japanese islands [i.e., the Soya, Tsugaru and Tsushima straits and the Shimonoseki Strait between Honshu and Kyushu] so that there should be no passage of Soviet submarines and other naval activities'. Nakasone also confirmed in 1983 that Japan accepted responsibility for the defence of its sea lanes out to 1,000 nautical miles, from Tokyo to Guam or from Osaka to the Strait of Taiwan, a concept that the JMSDF began promoting in the 1970s and which was first announced by Prime Minister Suzuki Zenko in Washington in May 1981.[7]

Since the end of the Cold War, when the Soviet navy was its primary preoccupation, the roles and missions of the JMSDF have been further expanded and amplified. The Russian navy is much less threatening than its Soviet predecessor, but the JMSDF now also has to contend with Chinese and North Korean naval capabilities and activities. Moreover, the JMSDF's purview now includes economic security, beyond the defence of SLOC, and even environmental security matters, in addition to its traditional military concerns. It shares with the Maritime Safety Agency responsibility for protection of Japan's EEZ, and the ocean and seabed resources within it. Its maritime surveillance activities now include the collection of economic intelligence. As Admiral Eiji Yoshikawa, the head of the JMSDF's Ominato Regional District Command, which is responsible for surveillance of Russian ships that pass through the Soya Strait, stated in 2004: 'National security is not limited just to military aspects, but must also include economic activities'. He said that monitoring of the Soya Strait would continue as vigilantly as during the Cold War: 'There will be no change in importance for our regional district headquarters of maintaining surveillance over the strait'. He also said that surveillance was 'not limited to ships of the Russian Pacific Fleet' but also included Russian oceanographic research ships and drilling ships searching for natural resources.[8]

---

6 Graham, *Japan's Sea Lane Security*, p. 101; and Auer, *Postwar Rearmament of Japanese Maritime Forces*, pp. 136, 159, 167.
7 Graham, *Japan's Sea Lane Security*, pp. 122–23, 143–44.
8 'Japanese Self-defence Forces to Keep Tabs on East Asia's Seabed', *Alexander's Gas & Oil Connections* (Vol. 9, No. 5), 10 March 2004, at www.gasandoil.com/goc/news/nts41021.htm

A litany of intrusions into Japan's EEZ and territorial waters since around 1996 is chronicled in chapter 2. These have primarily involved Chinese oceanographic and naval vessels, including submarines. Some have clearly been engaged in intelligence collection and oceanographic familiarisation in areas of strategic and operational importance in contingent circumstances, such as the Tsushimi, Tsugaru and Osumi straits, as well as areas subject to territorial disputes, such as the Senkaku Islands.

The JMSDF's ocean surveillance architecture, involving ground-based signals intelligence (SIGINT) and electronic intelligence (ELINT) collection systems, high frequency direction finding (HF DF) systems for locating communications transmitters at sea, and airborne collection systems such as long-range maritime patrol (LRMP) aircraft and maritime surveillance helicopters, as well as SOSUS (sound surveillance system)-type undersea submarine detection system, is described in chapter 3.

The Japanese Ground Self-Defense Force (JGSDF) also has important responsibilities with respect to coastal surveillance, especially in northern Hokkaido, with two HF/VHF (very high frequency) DF and six ELINT collection facilities located from Rebun Island and Wakkanai in the north-west to Nemuro in the north-east of the island. Two JGSDF stations for monitoring the south-western part of the Sea of Japan, separating North Korea from Honshu, were established in 2008, while a new coastal surveillance station is currently under construction on Yonaguni Island, Japan's westernmost point, close to the Senkaku Islands. These JGSDF assets are described in chapter 4.

The organisation of the JMSDF, including the high command, the fleet bases and the JMSDF's five regional district commands, within which its undersea and ELINT facilities are supported, is described in chapter 5. This chapter also describes the intelligence centres which serve the fleet HQ at Yokosuka, on the south-west side of Tokyo Bay, and the JMSDF's principal communications stations for connecting its ocean surveillance information collection facilities with the intelligence centres and fleet commands.

Subsequent chapters, while more technical, are essentially novel. They cover matters not addressed in the academic literature about Japanese defence policy. That literature is concerned with discourse about the cardinal aspects of declaratory policy, such as the interests and views of key defence decision-makers (especially the prime minister and the minister of defence); textual analyses of major official policy statements, such as white papers and successive mid-term defence programs; defence budget trends; current issues in the US–Japan alliance; and major equipment procurement programs, such as air warfare destroyers, helicopter carriers and submarines.

This study is meant to inform the debate, which is perhaps more narrow but certainly no less serious, concerned with issues of crisis stability and force employment policy. The China–Japan maritime relationship is exhibiting manifestations of action–reaction dynamics, or competitive arms acquisition processes, in which significant proportions of the ELINT and electronic warfare (EW) components of the respective acquisitions are tailored to the EW systems of the other side. Given that the possibilities for conflict are real, whether from accident, inadvertence or miscalculation, it is necessary to appreciate the capabilities that comprise the prevailing strategic balance or, in this case, the Japanese side of its undersea dimension. Close examination of these capabilities allows consideration of the prospective escalation dynamics once conflict is joined.

Appreciation of the technical parameters and performance characteristics of command, control, communications and intelligence systems is fundamental to sound strategic analysis. The analysis of antenna types and specifications allows ELINT and EW capabilities to be determined with reasonable precision. The geographic location of the antenna sites, at the entrances to Japan's various internal straits and waters, and given the limited ranges of most of the very high frequencies involved, allows prospective areas of conflict to be discerned.

Facilities that are of high strategic or operational value and also relatively vulnerable become lucrative targets; most of the shore stations for Japan's undersea submarine detection system and the associated ELINT facilities and communications centres are in this category. Some, particularly those co-located with other important command centres, may rank as nuclear targets in heuristic scenarios. Escalatory moves are likely to be attractive, making a significant difference in operational outcomes.

The United States would inevitably be a party to any such conflict at the outset. As described in chapter 8, the United States and Japan jointly maintain important submarine detection systems, including long segments of the so-called 'Fish Hook' undersea defence line, which monitors Chinese submarine movements in the East China Sea, while key elements of the US Ocean Surveillance Information System (OSIS) are co-located with JMSDF Ocean Surveillance Information System (JOSIS) facilities. Any degradation in US submarine detection and tracking capabilities would greatly compound the escalation dynamics. The strategy of the United States would dictate offensive actions against enemy submarines before these capabilities were operationally impaired.

2. Post-Cold War Intrusions into Japanese Waters

Chinese intrusions into Japan's claimed exclusive economic zone (EEZ), hitherto sporadic, increased rapidly after 1996, when Japan expanded its claims to include the disputed Senkaku Islands (called Diaoyu in Chinese) and other islands in the East China Sea, thus overlapping similar Chinese claims, as well as Okinotorishima in the Philippine Sea, midway between Taiwan and Guam.[1] Moreover, in addition to numerous deployments of 'oceanographic research' and signals intelligence (SIGINT) collection ships, the intrusions have increasingly involved warships, including submarines, sometimes acting aggressively.[2]

Chinese marine research vessels operated actively in Japan's EEZ 16 times in 1998, 30 times in 1999 and 24 times in 2000.[3] For example, the *Dongdiao* (V 232) oceanographic research/intelligence collection vessel was observed 'collecting electronic information off the coast of Japan' in February 2000.[4] In May 2000, the *Yanbing* (No. 723) AGI (Auxiliary General Intelligence), in an unprecedented move, passed through Japan's two most important straits, the Tsugaru Strait between Honshu and Hokkaido and the Tsushima Strait off Kyushu. (The vessel did not violate Japanese territorial waters in passing through the straits.)[5] In August 2000, a Chinese spy ship 'equipped with sophisticated electronic monitoring devices' penetrated inside Japan's 12-nautical-mile limit during a Chinese navy war game.[6] In January 2003 a Ming-class diesel submarine was 'detected inside Japan's waters' off the southern tip of Kyushu; it was reportedly 'collecting electronic intelligence and other oceanographic data'.[7] Another Ming-class submarine was observed in the Osumi Strait, about 40 kilometres south of Kyushu, on 12 November 2003.[8]

---

1   Yukie Yoshikawa, 'Okinotorishima: Just the Tip of the Iceberg', *Harvard Asia Quarterly* (Vol. 9, No. 4), 2006, pp. 51–61, at pranj.org/papers/yoshikawa-haq06.htm
2   Desmond Ball, 'Intelligence Collection Operations and EEZs: The Implications of New Technology', *Marine Policy* (Vol. 28), 2004, pp. 74–75.
3   National Institute for Defense Studies (NIDS), *East Asian Strategic Review 2001* (Tokyo, 2001), pp. 199–202.
4   James C. Bussert, 'Oil May be Focal Point of Sino-Japanese Dispute', *Signal*, November 2006, at www.afcea.org/signal/articles/anmviewer.asp?a=1216
5   NIDS, *East Asian Strategic Review 2001*, pp. 200–02; Rodger Baker, 'Spy Games: Japan, China Both Newly Ambitious in Asian Waters', *ABC News.Com*, 2 June 2000, at abcnews.go.com/sections/world/DailyNews/stratfor 000602.html; 'Editorial: Japan Responds to China Threat', *Taiwan News.Com*, 11 August 2001, at www.etaiwannews.com/Editorial/2001/08/11/997498010.htm
6   Charles R. Smith, 'Chinese Spy Ships Breach Japanese and Philippine Waters', *NewsMax.Com*, 9 April 2001, at www.newsmax.com/archives/articles/2001/4/8/195441.shtml
7   Bussert, 'Oil May be Focal Point of Sino-Japanese Dispute', at www.afcea.org/signal/articles/anmviewer.asp?a=1216
8   Iris Trang, 'China's Navy Floats a Warning to Taiwan', *Asia Times Online*, 25 November 2003, at atimes.com/atimes/China/EK25Ad01.html

Vociferous Japanese complaints to Beijing saw the rate of Chinese intrusions slow in 2001–03. The intrusions accelerated at the beginning of 2004, however, with 25 Chinese survey ships entering Japan's claimed EEZ during the first seven months of the year, a fourfold increase over 2003.[9] In July 2004, for example, a Yenlai-class marine survey ship and a Yanha-class AGI operated in Japan's EEZ.[10] Much of the increased activity concerned the area around Okinotori Island, which accounted for 12 incursions in 2004.[11] It was speculated that the People's Liberation Army (PLA) navy was 'surveying the seabed to support future PLAN submarine operations and preventing the U.S. Navy from coming to the defense of Taiwan'.[12] In December 2004, a Chinese ship was found 'using sonar, apparently to map the sea floor for Chinese submarine activities'.[13] In May 2005, Tokyo decided to install a surveillance radar on Okinotorishima to detect intruding vessels.[14]

In November 2004, Japanese Maritime Self-Defense Force (JMSDF) patrol aircraft near the Sakishima Islands detected a Han-class nuclear attack submarine (No. 405) underwater and tracked it for three days, including whilst it sailed submerged between Ishigaki and Miyako islands, at the southern end of the Ryukyu island chain.[15] In September 2005, a PLA navy five-ship surface action group, including a Sovremenny-class destroyer, two frigates, a replenishment ship, and the upgraded Dongdiao SIGINT/space event support ship (with its pennant number changed from 232 to 851), cruised near Okinotorishima.[16] In July 2006, the *Dong Fang Hong No. 2* marine research vessel was found inside

---

9   Toshu Noguchi, 'PRC Navy's Survey Operations Around Okinotori Island Increases by More Than Fourfold Over Last Year', *Sankei Shimbun*, 22 July 2004, cited in Richard Fisher, Jr., 'Growing Asymmetries in the China-Japan Naval Balance', 22 November 2005, at www.strategycenter.net/research/pubID.83/pub_detail.asp

10   Bussert, 'Oil May be Focal Point of Sino-Japanese Dispute', at www.afcea.org/signal/articles/anmviewer.asp?a=1216

11   'Chinese Ships Roam Around Okinotori Islands at Will', *Japan Today*, 8 December 2004, at www.japantoday.com/jp/shukan/257

12   Noguchi, cited in Fisher, 'Growing Asymmetries in the China-Japan Naval Balance', at www.strategycenter.net/research/pubID.83/pub_detail.asp

13   Yukie Yoshikawa, 'The US–Japan–China Mistrust Spiral and Okinotorishima', *Japan Focus*, 11 October 2007, at www.japanfocus.org/products/details/2541

14   ibid.

15   JMSDF, 'Precautionary Surveillance', at www.mod.go.jp/msdf/formal/english/surveillance/; 'Mystery Sub Sparks Japan Alert', *BBC News*, 10 November 2004, at news.bbc.co.uk/2/hi/3998107.stm; Jyh-Perng Wang & Ing-Chyi Jan, 'On the Event of PRC Han-class Sub Intruding Japan and Conferring the Proper Thoughts of Taiwan Defense', *Taiwan Defense Affairs* (Vol. 5, No. 4), Summer 2005, pp. 72–105; Kenneth B. Sherman, 'Mystery Sub Detected Off Japanese Coast', *Journal of Electronic Defense* (Vol. 28, No. 1), January 2005, p. 24; Peter A. Dutton, 'International Law and the November 2004 *Han* Incident', *Asian Security* (Vol. 2, No. 2), 2006, pp. 87–101.

16   Fisher, 'Growing Asymmetries in the China-Japan Naval Balance', at www.strategycenter.net/research/pubID.83/pub_detail.asp; Bussert, 'Oil May be Focal Point of Sino-Japanese Dispute', at www.afcea.org/signal/articles/anmviewer.asp?a=1216; James E. Fanell, 'China: Big Trouble on the High Seas', *Hoover Digest* (No. 3), 2006, at www.hoover.org/publications/digest/4635601.html

Japan's claimed EEZ, just 24 kilometres south-west of Uotsuri, the main island in the Senkakus.[17] In February 2007, the *Dong Fang Hong No. 2* returned to the Senkakus; it was detected 30 kilometres west of Uotsuri Island.[18]

In September 2008, an 'unidentified' (but almost certainly Chinese) submarine was detected south of the entrance to the Bungo Strait between Kyushu and Shikoku Islands; it was some 60 kilometres south-west of Cape Ashizuri, Shikoku's southernmost point, and 7 kilometres inside Japan's territorial waters. The submarine was spotted with 'a periscope-like object' poking out of the water, and was evidently on a reconnaissance mission.[19] And, five weeks later, four Chinese naval vessels, including a destroyer, passed through the Tsugaru Strait; they were found by P-3C surveillance aircraft on 19 October about 35 kilometres off Tappi Zaki.[20]

In September 2009, a foreign submarine was detected off the Pacific coast of Kochi Prefecture on the southern side of Shikoku Island. Beijing denied that it was a Chinese submarine, but Japanese naval authorities insisted that it was.[21] In April 2010, two Chinese submarines and eight destroyers were detected between Okinawa Island and Miyako-jima. The fleet conducted refuelling and engaged in helicopter operations in an area about 140 kilometres west-south-west of Okinawa. One of the helicopters flew within about 90 metres of the *Suzunami*, a Japanese destroyer that was monitoring the activities of the Chinese warships.[22]

On 7 September 2010, a Chinese fishing trawler, the *Minjinyu 5179*, deliberately rammed two Japanese Coast Guard vessels near the Senkaku Islands. The 14-man crew was detained and released six days later, but the captain was detained until 24 September, in the face of vehement objections from Beijing.[23] A Chinese Foreign Ministry spokeswoman said that 'Japan's actions have violated international law and rudimentary common sense in international matters', and that 'they are absurd, illegal and invalid', and warned that 'if Japan continues in this reckless fashion, it will taste its own bitter fruit'. China cancelled planned talks with Japan over the Okinotorishima dispute, and warned of 'worse

---

17   Fanell, 'China: Big Trouble on the High Seas', at www.hoover.org/publications/digest/4635601.html

18   'Tokyo Protests Chinese Surveillance Near Islands', *Taipei Times*, 6 February 2007, p. 4.

19   'Unidentified Submarine Detected Between Shikoku and Kyushu', *Japan Times*, 15 September 2008.

20   'Chinese Destroyer Sailed Through Tsugaru Strait', *Daily Yomiuri Online*, 22 October 2008, at www.yomiuri.co.jp/dy/national/20081022TDY02307.htm

21   'Japan Ends Hunt for Submarine Intruder', *Defense News*, 18 September 2009, at www.defensenews.com/story.php?i=3726554

22   'MSDF Tracks China Armada Off Okinawa', *Japan Times*, 14 April 2010, at www.japantimes.co.jp/text/nn20100414a2.html

23   Sourabh Gupta, 'China-Japan Trawler Incident: Reviewing the Dispute Over Senkaku/Daioyu Waters', *East Asia Forum*, 6 December 2010, at www.eastasiaforum.org/2010/12/06/china-japan-trawler-incident-review-of-legalities-understandings-and-practices-in-disputed-senkakudaioyu-waters/

repercussions'.[24] As of 7 September, there were 160 Chinese vessels fishing in the area, of which 30 were 'inside what Japan claims to be its territorial waters'.[25] On 14 October, China dispatched two fisheries patrol boats to the area to protect 'the legal rights of Chinese fishermen'. The boats were spotted again on 24 October, after which Japan lodged an official protest with Beijing.[26]

In June 2011, the Chinese navy conducted its largest-ever exercise in the Pacific. Eleven ships – three Sovremenny-class destroyers, one Jiangkai II-class frigate, one Jiang-wei II frigate, two Jiang-wei I frigates, a Fuqing-class oiler, a Dajiang-class auxiliary submarine rescue vessel, a Tuzhong-class fleet tug, and a Dongdiao-class electronic intelligence ship – passed through the Ryukyu island chain about 100 kilometres north-east of Myako-jima on 8–9 June, and returned through the Japanese islands on 22–23 June. The exercise was conducted about 450 kilometres south-west of Okinotorishima, and included seaborne replenishment, gunnery practice, helicopter flight training and use of unmanned aerial vehicles (UAV).[27]

On 23 June the *Nan Feng*, a research ship belonging to the Chinese Academy of Fishery Sciences (CAFS) was found conducting surveys within Japan's EEZ about 330 kilometres from Miyagi City in north-eastern Honshu. When questioned by Japanese Coast Guard vessels, the *Nan Feng* said that 'it was collecting water at public sea for environmental and fishery studies'.[28]

On 24 August 2011, Tokyo formally protested to Beijing after two Chinese ships briefly entered what it regards as its territorial waters near the Senkakus. The Chinese Foreign Minister responded that China's sovereignty over the islands was 'indisputable', and said that the boats were in the area to 'maintain normal order' for fishing.[29]

China conducted another large exercise in the western Pacific in November 2011. Six vessels, including the intelligence-gathering *Beidiao 900* (a Type 814A Dadie-class surveillance ship), missile frigates and supply ships, passed through the waters between Okinawa and Miyako-jima on 22–23 November

---

24 Chris Buckley, 'China Cancels Japan Talks, Warns on Sea Dispute', *International Business Times*, 11 September 2010, at m.ibtimes.com/china-japan-sea-61413.html
25 'China Warns Japan Over Trawler Seizure', *RTT News*, 10 September 2010, at www.rttnews.com/Content/GeneralNews.aspx?Id=1414654&SM=1
26 'Japan Protests to China Over Boats Near Islands', *AFP*, 25 October 2010, at www.aaj.tv/2010/10/japan-protests-to-china-over-boats-near-islands/
27 Huang Jing-jing, 'Chinese Navy Fleet Completes Largest-ever Training in Pacific', *Want China Times*, 25 June 2011, at www.wantchinatimes.com/news-subclass-cnt.aspx?id=20110625000003&cid=1101; James Simpson, 'Chinese UAV Spotted by MSDF Aircraft', *Japan Security Watch*, 30 June 2011, at newpacificinstitute.org/jsw/?p=6844
28 Huang Jing-jing, 'Chinese Navy Fleet Completes Largest-ever Training in Pacific', at www.wantchinatimes.com/news-subclass-cnt.aspx?id=20110625000003&cid=1101
29 'Japan Protests Over China Ships in Disputed Waters', *Reuters*, 24 August 2011, at www.reuters.com/article/2011/08/24/us-japan-china-disputes-idUSTRE77N0R620110824

on their way to the exercise. Chinese authorities said that these were 'routine manoeuvers' and that China's freedom of navigation 'shall not be subject to any form of hindrance'.[30] In mid-December, China's largest and most advanced ocean surveillance vessel, the new *Maritime Surveillance 50*, cruised around disputed waters in the East Sea 'to protect the rights of navigation in the waters'.[31] In January 2012, to China's chagrin, Japan decided to name 39 uninhabited islands, mostly located around the Senkakus, as 'the basis for defining Japan's EEZ'.[32]

In early February 2012, four Chinese frigates passed through the Miyako Strait between Okinawa and Miyako-jima to conduct exercises in the western Pacific.[33] Three vessels passed through the Osumi Strait south of Kyushu on 30 April; China's Defence Ministry said that the passage was 'routine and non-threatening', and 'not targeted at any specific country or objective'.[34] Another three passed through the Osumi Strait on 13 June, which Beijing again said was 'regular training not aimed at specific targets or nations'.[35] Seven navy vessels transited the Miyako Strait to the Pacific on 4 October, returning to the East China Sea through the strait between Taiwan and Yonaguni on 17 October.[36] Five navy ships passed through the Miyako Strait for 'a routine training exercise' in the western Pacific on 28 November 2012.[37]

Tensions again flared at the Senkaku Islands in September 2012. On 14 September, six Chinese surveillance vessels entered waters near the disputed islands. China's Foreign Ministry said that the ships were present 'to carry out maritime surveillance' and to perform 'law enforcement over its [China's] maritime rights'. On 18 September, 12 surveillance vessels were operating in the area, three of which 'sailed into Japanese territorial waters'.[38] All of these had left the area

---

30 'Talk of the Day: China to Conduct Pacific Naval Drills', *Focus Taiwan*, 24 November 2011, at focustaiwan. tw/ShowNews/WebNews_Detail.aspx?Type=aIPL&ID=201111240049

31 走进"中国海监50"号的"心脏" ['Walking into the "Heart" of "China Maritime Surveillance 50"'], *Xinhua*, 15 December 2011, at news.xinhuanet.com/mil/2011-12/15/c_122429657.htm; 'China's Largest Ocean Surveillance Ship and Helicopter Coordinated the First East China Sea Cruise', 15 December 2011, at www.3abc.net/?p=25063

32 'Japan Plans to Name 39 Islets in Disputed, Remote Waters', *Global Times*, 17 January 2012, at www. globaltimes.cn/NEWS/tabid/99/ID/692425/Japan-plans-to-name-39-islets-in-disputed-remote-waters.aspx.

33 J. Michael Cole, 'PLA Sorties Threaten Encirclement', *Taipei Times*, 9 February 2012, at www.taipeitimes. com/News/front/archives/2012/02/09/2003525025

34 'China Says its Naval Vessels' Transit of Osumi Strait Not Threatening', *Mainichi*, 2 May 2012, at mainichi. jp/english/english/newsselect/news/20120502p2g00m0dm019000c.html

35 'Japan Concerned after Chinese Vessels Seen Again in Osumi Strait', *Want China Times*, 16 June 2012, at www.wantchinatimes.com/news-subclass-cnt.aspx?id=20120616000062&cid=1101

36 'Yin Zhuo: China Doesn't Need to Inform Japan When Passing Through Miyako Strait', *People's Daily Online*, 12 October 2012, at english.peopledaily.com.cn/90786/7974501.html; 'Seven Chinese Navy Warships Skirt Okinawa', *Japan Times*, 17 October 2012, at www.japantimes.co.jp/text/nn20121017a3

37 'Chinese Navy Fleet Enters West Pacific for Routine Training', *Xinhua*, 28 November 2012, at news. xinhuanet.com/english/china/2012-11/28/c_132005111.htm

38 'Update: China Surveillance Ships Enter Disputed Waters with Japan', *Asahi Shimbun*, 14 September 2012, at ajw.asahi.com/article/behind_news/politics/AJ201209140023; '14 Chinese Vessels Spotted Near Senkakus but No Fishing Ship Armada', *Asahi Shimbun*, 19 September 2012, at ajw.asahi.com/article/behind_ news/politics/AJ201209190059

by 24 September, but frequent deployments resumed in October. Four Chinese maritime patrol ships entered 'Japanese territorial waters' around the Senkakus on 3 October and remained in the area for more than a week, despite statements by Japan's Foreign Ministry that their intrusions were 'unacceptable'.[39] Another four Chinese patrol vessels entered Japanese waters on 20 October; they stayed for 11 days, while the Japanese Government 'strongly protested' and China's Foreign Ministry stated that China was prepared to 'respond forcefully' if Japan challenged its sovereignty over the islands.[40]

On 19 January 2013, the tensions over the Senkakus reached their highest point when Chinese navy ships directed their fire-control radars onto a Japanese helicopter and a JMSDF destroyer (the *Yudachi* DD-103) on 30 January. The radars were turned on for 'a matter of minutes'. The incidents were the closest the two countries have come to exchanging fire. The Chinese Government initially denied that any fire-control radars had been used, while the Japanese Government considered releasing tape recordings of the radar emissions, but decided that would compromise its electronic intelligence (ELINT) collection capabilities. Chinese officials admitted in March that a fire-control radar had in fact been used, but said that it was 'accidental' and 'the act was not planned'.[41]

On 4 February 2013, two Chinese Hai Jian-class maritime surveillance vessels harassed two Japanese fishing boats near Uotsurishima Island, the largest of the Senkakus and well inside Japan's claimed territorial waters.[42] On 18 February, three Hai Jian-class vessels chased another Japanese fishing boat around Uotsurishima Island.[43]

---

39   'Tokyo Lashes Out About Chinese Ships in Territorial Waters', *Japan Daily Press*, 4 October 2012, at   japandailypress.com/tokyo-lashes-out-about-chinese-ships-in-territorial-waters-0414398/;   'Chinese Government States it Will Continue Patrolling Senkaku Waters', *Japan Daily Press*, 9 October 2012, at japandailypress.com/chinese-government-states-it-will-continue-patrolling-senkaku-waters-0915067/0

40   'Chinese Patrol Ships Enter Japan Territorial Waters Again', *Asahi Shimbun*, 25 October 2012, at ajw. asahi.com/article/behind_news/politics/AJ201210250060; 'Chinese Ships in Territorial Waters Near Senkaku, Once Again', *Japan Daily Press*, 25 October 2012, at japandailypress.com/chinese-ships-in-territorial-waters-near-senkaku-once-again-2517289/; 'Another Day, Another 4 Chinese Ships in Japan's Territorial Waters', *Japan Daily Press*, 30 October 2012, at japandailypress.com/another-day-another-4-chinese-ships-in-japans-territorial-waters-3017556/; 'China Threatens Force if Japan Challenges Sovereignty', *RIA Novosti*, 27 October 2012, at en.rian.ru/world/20121027/176955713.html

41   Martin Fackler, 'Japan Says China Aimed Military Radar at Ship', *New York Times*, 5 February 2013; 'Senkaku/Diaoyu Islands: Japan May Release China Radar Data', *BBC News*, 9 February 2013, at www.bbc. co.uk/news/world-asia-21392248; 'Japan Mulling Over Release of Chinese Radar Data in Senkaku Row', *Japan Daily Press*, 11 February 2013, at japandailypress.com/japan-mulling-over-release-of-chinese-radar-data-in-senkaku-row-1123103/; 'Chinese Officials Admit to MSDF Radar Lock Allegations', *Japan Times*, 18 March 2013, at www.japantimes.co.jp/news/2013/03/18/national/chinese-officials-admit-to-msdf-radar-lock-allegations/

42   Yuzo Hisatsune, 'Chinese Boats Harass Japanese Fishing Vessels Near Senkakus', *Asahi Shimbun*, 28 February 2013, at ajw.asahi.com/article/asia/china/AJ201302280058

43   Ryuji Kudo & Tsukasa Kimura, 'Three Chinese Vessels Pursue Japanese Fishing Boat Near Senkakus', *Asahi Shimbun*, 21 February 2013, at ajw.asahi.com/article/behind_news/social_affairs/AJ201302210082

On 17 February, Chinese vessels deployed a series of buoys around the islands. China's Foreign Ministry said that their purpose was to carry out 'maritime weather observations', but Japanese authorities were concerned that they were intended 'to collect intelligence about Japanese operations', and particularly 'to detect movement of submarines'.[44]

On 2 May 2013, an unidentified submerged submarine was detected close to Amami-Oshima, an island roughly halfway between Kyushu and Okinawa. On 12 May, another 'foreign submarine' was detected just outside Japan's territorial waters south of Kume-jima in Okinawa Prefecture. Prime Minister Shinzo Abe said that he was 'not going to mention the nationality of the submarine, but we have already carried out the necessary analysis, including about its nationality', and that 'we want the relevant country to be aware that this must never happen again'. A 'government source' reportedly said that 'the sub likely belonged to the Chinese Navy'.[45]

On 13–14 July, five Chinese navy vessels (two destroyers, two frigates and a supply ship) passed through the Soya Strait from west to east, exiting into the Pacific Ocean. This was the first time that China's naval ships had 'ventured into that waterway'.[46] The warships returned to Qingdao, the headquarters of the North China Sea Fleet, through the Miyako Strait between Okinawa and Miyako-jima on 25 July. A senior officer at the PLA's Academy of Military Science noted that 'the Chinese navy has the capability to cut the first island chain into several pieces', and that 'Now the chain is fragmented'.[47]

On 7 November, four Chinese Coast Guard vessels entered Japan's territorial waters off one of the Senkaku Islands. They reportedly remained in the area for about 90 minutes.[48] Tensions escalated again in November when the JMSDF conducted a large, 18-day exercise in Japan's southern islands. The exercise, conducted from 1 to 18 November, involved 34,000 military personnel, six vessels, 360 aircraft, and six Type-88 surface-to-ship missiles. Two of the Type-88s, together with a launching system, were deployed to Miyako-jima on 6 November. Four, together with another launcher, were deployed to Naha air base in Okinawa on 7 November. The missiles effectively covered the 300

44 Martin Fackler, 'Chinese Buoys are Focus of Latest Dispute Over Contested Islands', *New York Times*, 22 February 2013; 'Japan Questions Chinese Buoys Near Senkakus', *Japan Daily Press*, 27 February 2013, at japandailypress.com/japan-questions-chinese-buoys-near-senkakus-2724166/

45 'Foreign Sub Spotted Near Japan's Territorial Waters', *Asahi Shimbun*, 14 May 2013; and 'Foreign Submarine Spotted Near Japan's Territorial Waters', *Japan Daily Press*, 14 May 2013, at japandailypress.com/foreign-submarine-spotted-near-japanese-territorial-waters-1428827/

46 Kirk Spitzer, 'China Finds a Gap in Japan's Maritime Chokepoints', *Time*, 18 July 2013, at nation.time.com/2013/07/18/china-finds-a-gap-in-japans-maritime-chokepoints/

47 'China Sails Through "First Island Chain"', *China Daily*, 2 August 2013, at usa.chinadaily.com.cn/china/2013-08/02/content_16863855.htm

48 'Japan Installing Missiles on Pacific Gateway Islands', *Taipei Times*, 8 November 2013, at www.taipeitimes.com/News/front/archives/2013/11/08/2003576391

kilometres between Okinawa and Miyako-jima, used by Chinese navy vessels to transit into and out of the western Pacific. The Chinese media reported that deployment of the missiles to Miyako-jima was 'an unprecedented move … targeted at blocking the Chinese Navy' and 'can pose real threats to the Chinese Navy'.[49]

North Korean Intrusions into Japanese Waters

North Korean penetrations into Japanese waters have been much more irregular, with major incidents involving 'spy ships' in 1999 and 2001. On 23 March 1999, two 'suspicious vessels' (bearing the false names *No. 1 Taesei Maru* and *No. 2 Yamato Maru*) were found by a JMSDF P-3C Orion off the Noto Peninsula in Honshu's Ishikawa Prefecture, across the Sea of Japan from North Korea. On 24 March, the JMSDF was authorised to take 'maritime security action' to stop and inspect the boats. JMSDF destroyers and patrol aircraft fired warning shots – the first time that Japanese ships or aircraft had fired warning shots since 1953, when a patrol boat intercepted a Soviet spy ship off Cape Soya on the northern tip of Hokkaido. The two North Korean ships were pursued by the JMSDF destroyers until they crossed Japan's Air Defence Identification Zone (ADIZ), after which they berthed in Chongjin in the northern part of North Korea.[50] On 22 December 2001, the Japan Coast Guard (JCG) (formerly the Maritime Safety Agency) sank a 'suspicious' North Korean boat, with the loss of its 15 crewmen, in complicated and controversial circumstances; the boat was within Japan's EEZ, but well outside Japan's territorial waters, west of the Japanese island of Amami-Oshima, between Kyushu and Okinawa.[51]

In January 2002, the JDA compiled a list of 27 'suspicious' ships that had been sighted operating in waters around Japan in recent years. Some of them belonged to China and Russia, but the majority were classified as North Korean ships. The North Korean ships featured 'multiple antennas, double doors in the stern to launch and retrieve smaller craft, and an engine mounted forward rather than aft, as is usually the case'.[52]

---

49 ibid.
50 'Probe Into the Responses Made by the Government to Suspicious Boats', *Asahi Shimbun*, 7 April 1999, in American Embassy, Tokyo, 'Daily Summary of Japanese Press', 12 April 1999, at www.usc.edu/isd/archives/dsjp/summaries/1999/April/Sm990412.doc; Ball, 'Intelligence Collection Operations and EEZs', pp. 75–76.
51 Ball, 'Intelligence Collection Operations and EEZs', p. 76.
52 '27 "Spy" Ships Operating in Waters Around Japan', *Spy Tech Agency: Intel Bulletin*, 4 January 2002, at www.spytechagency.com/Inte%20Bulletin/Intel%20Bulletin%20020020104.htm; Alex Berkofsky, 'Tokyo Turns Up the Military Heat', *Asia Times Online*, 16 January 2002, at www.atimes.com/japan-econ/DA16Dh01.html

The Dispute with South Korea over Dokdo (Takeshima)

Japan also has an outstanding dispute with South Korea over ownership of Dokdo or Takeshima, a group of islands in the southern part of the Sea of Japan, about halfway between the two countries, which sometimes causes friction between them.[53] The islands were annexed by Japan in 1905, primarily because the Imperial Japanese Navy (IJN) was interested in their utility for watchtowers and a telegraph station.[54] The main island is currently occupied by South Korea, which has built lodgings, lighthouses and a 'monitoring facility' there.[55]

The area is watched closely by both the JMSDF and the JCG, however, and incursions by South Korean survey vessels into the disputed waters are regularly protested. In July 2006, for example, a South Korean survey ship was intercepted by a Japanese patrol boat in the area; Japan asked South Korea to withdraw the vessel, but in the ensuing 'war of words' a South Korean Government spokesman said that 'it is the basic right and prerogative of this country to conduct any scientific research within our exclusive economic zone area'.[56] The dispute over Dokdo flared up again in July 2008 after Tokyo reaffirmed its claim on the area. South Korea stepped up its air surveillance patrols and despatched an additional patrol boat to the area.[57]

Issues with Taiwan

Japan also has discordant issues with Taiwan, some arising from the sovereignty dispute over the Senkaku Islands, which Taiwan also claims, together with China, and some from zealous enforcement by the JCG of strict laws concerning foreign fishing in Japan's territorial waters. On 10 June 2008, a JCG patrol vessel rammed and sank a Taiwanese sports fishing boat near the Senkakus; the crew were detained in Ishigaki for two days 'for questioning'.[58] On 16 November

---

53   Joseph Morgan & Mark Valencia, *Atlas for Marine Policy in East Asian Seas* (University of California, Berkeley, 1992), pp. 29–31.

54   'Japan's Takeshima X-Files', at dokdo-takeshima.com/dokdo-x-files2.html

55   'Seoul's Spat with Tokyo Boils Over', *Bangkok Post*, 15 July 2008, p. 4.

56   'South Korea Survey Angers Japan', *BBC News*, 3 July 2006, at news.bbc.co.uk/2/hi/asia-pacific/5139726. stm; 'Japan Asks S Korea to End Survey', *BBC News*, 5 July 2006, at news.bbc.co.uk/2/hi/asia-pacific/5149048. stm

57   'Seoul's Spat with Tokyo Boils Over', *Bangkok Post*, 15 July 2008, p. 4.

58   Ministry of Foreign Affairs, Taipei, 'Crew of Sport Fishing Boat Lienhe to Return Home Safely', 19 June 2008, at www.mofa.gov.tw/webapp/ct.asp?xItem=32138&ctNode=761&mp=1

2008 a Taiwanese fishing boat, the *Yungsheng No. 106*, was detained by the JCG after being chased and rammed near Miyako-jima; it was taken, together with its crew, to Hirara, the main town on Miyako-jima, 'for an investigation'.[59]

On 13 September 2009, when another Taiwanese sports fishing boat was impounded and its crew detained by the JCG after it had been found in waters near Miyako-jima, five Taiwanese National Coast Guard Administration (NCGA) vessels confronted five JCG patrol ships in what was described in the Taiwanese media as 'the first naval encounter between Taiwan and Japan'.[60] In September 2010, Japanese navy ships forced a Taiwanese vessel carrying 'activists' to the Senkakus to turn back and return to Taiwan.[61] In September 2012, 'about 40' Taiwanese fishing boats, accompanied by eight NCGA vessels, entered disputed waters near the Senkakus, but were turned away after JCG and NCGA vessels engaged in a duel with water cannons.[62]

59 'Japan Seizes Taiwanese Fishing Boat in Miyakos', *Taipei Times*, 17 November 2008, at www.taipeitimes.com/News/taiwan/archives/2008/11/17/2003428846; 'Taiwan Fishing Boat Detained by Japanese Coast Guard', *BBC Monitoring International Reports*, 16 November 2008, at www.encyclopedia.com/doc/1G1-189045422.html; Ministry of the Interior, Taipei, 'Japan Authorities Release Taiwanese Fishing Boat, Crew', 19 November 2008, at www.moi.gov.tw/English/latest_news_detail.aspx?type=taiwan&sn=626
60 'Taiwan Boat Seized', *China Post*, 15 September 2009, at www.chinapost.com.tw/taiwan/national/national-news/2009/09/15/224652/Taiwan-boat.htm; 'Foreign Ministry Asks Japan to Release Seized Boat', *China Post*, 17 September 2009, at www.chinapost.com.tw/taiwan/foreign-affairs/2009/09/17/224954/Foreign-ministry.htm
61 'Japanese Navy Force Taiwan Boat Back from Disputed Islands', *Asia News*, 14 September 2010, at www.asianews.it/news-en/Japanese-navy-force-Taiwan-boat-back-from-disputed-islands-19453.html
62 'Taiwan, Japan in High-Seas Standoff', *Taipei Times*, 26 September 2012; Kiyoshi Takenaka & Kaori Kaneko, 'Japan Fires Water Cannon to Turn Away Taiwan Boats', *Reuters*, 25 September 2012, at www.reuters.com/article/2012/09/25/us-china-japan-taiwan-idUSBRE88O02C20120925

3. The JMSDF's Ocean Surveillance Architecture

The Japanese Maritime Self-Defense Force (JMSDF) has a comprehensive architecture of ocean surveillance systems for monitoring the disparate challenges it faces in supporting its defensive activities, including SOSUS (sound surveillance system)-type submarine detection and tracking systems, high frequency direction finding (HF DF) facilities, ocean surveillance ships, and maritime surveillance aircraft. Information from all of these systems is integrated into the JMSDF's Ocean Surveillance Information System (JOSIS), the current version of which is officially called the JMSDF OSIS Evolutionary Development (JOED) system, at the JMSDF's Fleet HQ at Yokosuka, in Kanagawa Prefecture, on the western side of Tokyo Bay.

Japan's undersea surveillance network, as a report in May 2003 noted, provides a '24-hour non-stop undersea surveillance and listening' capability.[1] It consists of about 30 passive hydrophone arrays, connected to some 14 or more shore stations. The underwater surveillance systems were designed initially for harbour defence, and then to monitor movements through Japan's internal and adjacent straits; several of them involve long-range, deep-water systems (connected to shore stations at Matsumae, in south-western Hokkaido; Higashidori on the Shimokita Peninsula, in the north-east of Honshu; and White Beach in Okinawa). Magnetic measurement systems have also been deployed on the sea floor across the Tsugaru and Tsushima straits, while magnetic measurement stations have been established at Osaka Bay and Sasebo Bay. The latter are avowedly for measuring the magnetic signatures and degaussing of minehunters, but they are also able to detect submarines entering these two key areas.

Japan now has eight signals intelligence (SIGINT) stations equipped with circularly disposed antenna arrays (CDAA) for both signals interception and HF DF activities. Three large and sensitive CDAAs provide bearings on intercepted signals with reasonable accuracy. The first, which became operational in 1977, is located at Miho, on Honshu's west coast in Tottori Prefecture; it is Japan's main SIGINT station for monitoring signals in North Korea. The second, constructed in 1987, is at Chitose, in Hokkaido, which is the main station for intercepting signals in the Russian Far East. The third, which was constructed in 2004–05 and became operational in 2006, is located on Kikai-jima, near Amami-Oshima Island, about midway between Kyushu and Okinawa; it is primarily concerned with intercepting Chinese signals. Five 7-element CDAAs are located

---

1 'After Taking Office, Koizumi Quietly Expands Japan's Self-Defence Force, Improves Weaponry', 20 May 2003, at japan.people.com.cn/2003/5/21/200352192116.htm

at Wakkanai, at the north-western tip of Hokkaido; Nemuro, in the north-east corner of Hokkaido; Kobunato, in Niigata Prefecture, on the shore of the Sea of Japan; Tachiarai, in the northern part of Kyushu; and Ishigaki, at the southern end of the Ryukyu archipelago.

The JMSDF operates several ocean surveillance and SIGINT collection ships, including the *Nichinan* AGS/AGI, the *Shonan* AGS and two SURTASS (Surveillance Towed Array Sensor System) acoustic measurement (or underwater listening) ships. It has the second-largest fleet of maritime surveillance aircraft in the world (after the US Navy), comprising P-3C Orion long-range maritime patrol (LRMP) aircraft and SH-60J Sea Hawk patrol helicopters. It also has five EP-3 SIGINT aircraft, based at Iwakuni, together with an associated Electronic Data Analysis Department.

In addition, the Maritime Security Agency (MSA), now officially called the Japan Coast Guard, has also greatly expanded since 1948 in terms of both its capabilities and its roles and missions. It possesses a large fleet of patrol vessels, provides hydrographic and navigation aids services, maintains HF DF stations and more modern digital communications facilities for monitoring maritime distress signals, and has expanded its responsibilities to include 'securing the safety of the sea-lanes' and 'maintaining order on the seas'.[2]

The 5th Research Center (also called the Naval Systems Research Center) of the Ministry of Defense's (MoD) Technical Research and Development Institute (TRDI), based at Nagase in Yokosuka, also has expertise and capabilities with respect to undersea detection activities. Its 1st Division specialises in the development of sonar and underwater acoustics systems, and its Kawasaki Branch develops magnetic sensors.[3] The TRDI has a specially built experimental ship, the *Kurihama* ASE 6101, and an Experimental Center at Higashidori on Shimokita Peninsula, adjacent to the JMSDF's Shimokita-hanto Ocean Observation Station.

The JMSDF's ocean surveillance capabilities are greatly augmented by cooperation and exchange arrangements with the US Navy. Unlike the Japanese Air Self-Defense Force (JASDF) and the US Air Force (USAF) with respect to air defence, where the JASDF resolutely resisted cooperation until as recently as 2005, the JMSDF has, since its establishment, cooperated extensively with the US Navy. This has included operational cooperation with respect to undersea

---

2   Richard J. Samuels, '"New Fighting Power": Japan's Growing Maritime Capabilities and East Asian Security', *International Security* (Vol. 32, No. 3), Winter 2007/08, pp. 84–112.
3   US Congress, Office of Technology Assessment (OTA), *Holding the Edge: Maintaining the Defense Technology Base, Volume 2 – Appendices* (OTA-ISC-432, January 1990), Appendix H, 'Strategic Technology Management in Japan: Commercial-Military Comparisons', p. 180.

surveillance and anti-submarine warfare (ASW) activities. In the late 1950s, the US Navy expedited equipment for the JMSDF's coastal defence stations guarding the entrances to Tokyo and Sasebo bays.

In the early 1980s, the JMSDF and the US Navy agreed on an effective division of labour, whereby the former would focus on ASW and the ability to block Soviet naval access to the Soya, Tsugaru and Tsushima straits, while the US Navy concentrated on offensive operations.[4] A review in 1996 noted that 'the two navies share information, technology, equipment, supplies and resources; they work, operate, and train together; and they trust, respect and depend on each other'.[5]

US Navy and contractor personnel participate directly in some of the JMSDF's surveillance activities. For example, US technical crews operate the sensor equipment aboard the JMSDF's two SURTASS ships, and data collected by these ships are shared with the US Navy.[6] A small team of about six to seven US Navy personnel were stationed at the JMSDF's Matsumae SOSUS station in the 1980s and 1990s.[7] At Yokosuka, a joint JMSDF–US Navy Project 6100 office, assisted by personnel from E-Systems in Dallas, Texas, manages three SOSUS-type systems.[8]

Management and coordination of cooperative activities has been greatly facilitated by the co-location of the US Navy's 7th Fleet HQ with the HQ of the JMSDF Fleet at Yokosuka. The US base is a nodal point in the navy's Ocean Surveillance Information System (OSIS), which provides intelligence from its worldwide networks of SOSUS facilities, HF DF stations, airborne systems, and ocean surveillance satellites (formerly called *Classic Wizard* and now *Intruder*, and for which a down-link station code-named *ICEBox* is located near Misawa, in north-east Honshu). The JMSDF's JOED centre exchanges data directly with the US system. The JOED computer networks are managed by Litton PRC, now a subsidiary of Northrop Grumman Corporation.[9]

---

4   Graham, *Japan's Sea Lane Security, 1940–2004*, chapter 5.
5   Naoyuki Agawa & James E. Auer, 'Pacific Friendship', *U.S. Naval Institute Proceedings*, October 1996, p. 56.
6   Norman Friedman, *The Naval Institute Guide to World Naval Weapons Systems, 1997–1998* (Naval Institute Press, Annapolis, Maryland, 1997), pp. 21, 24; 'Japan–U.S. Security Treaty After 50 Years – Phantom Alliance: U.S. Servicemen in the Shadows; Watching Behind Weapons Guidance', *Tokyo Shimbun*, 24 August 2001, in American Embassy, Tokyo, 'Daily Summary of Japanese Press', 28 August 2001.
7   『北海度のC3I基地に見る新たな福強と変化』、松井愈（著者）、1993年日本平和会国際会議、C3I分科会・18th　全道基地闘争活動者会議（93・10）[Matsui Masaru, 'Looking at New Developments and Changes in Hokkaido C³I Bases, Japan Peace Committee International Conference, C3I Sub-committee; and 18th National Base Struggle Activists Conference (October 1993)', Hokkaido Peace Committee Study Document No. 26, 8–1994], pp. 4–5.
8   'Sea-bottom Cable-laying Ship Operating Offshore: Fishermen Witnessed in About 1972', in 'Report: The Unsinkable Aircraft Carrier Archipelago – Behind the Tomahawk Deployment', *Asahi Shimbun*, 17 June 1984.
9   'CV: Senior Systems Security Engineer', 11 August 2007, at space-careers.com/agency/cvview_7971.html

The JMSDF's *Kongo*-class air warfare destroyers, equipped with the US Navy's *Aegis* combat system and AN/SPY-1D search radar, exchange air and missile tracking data directly with US Navy *Aegis* ships stationed in the western Pacific. Four *Kongo*-class destroyers were commissioned in the 1990s; a fifth was commissioned in 2007, and a sixth joined the fleet in 2009. On 18 December 2007, the *Kongo* (DDG 173) detected, tracked and successfully engaged a ballistic missile target launched from the US Navy's Pacific Missile Range Facility on Kauai in Hawaii.[10]

---

10   William Cole, 'In Test, Japan Warship Blasts Missile Launched from Kauai', *Honolulu Advertiser*, 18 December 2007, at the.honoluluadvertiser.com/article/2007/Dec/18/ln/hawaii712180346.html

4. The Japanese Ground Self-Defense Force (JGSDF)

The Japanese Ground Self-Defense Force (JGSDF) also has substantial responsibilities and capabilities for coastal surveillance and coastal defence, especially with respect to northern Hokkaido. These responsibilities have been maintained through adroit bureaucratic–political manoeuvring, but their origins go back to the early part of the 20th century when, in 1907, two years after the Imperial Japanese Navy's decisive defeat of the Russian Baltic Fleet in the Battle of Tsushima, the army 'reasserted its control over the determination of the nation's strategic priorities', with Russia being formally identified as 'Japan's prime hypothetical enemy' and the army's forward position on the Asian continent being Japan's 'basic strategy'.[1] Through the 1920s and 1930s, while the navy looked eastwards towards the United States and southwards with respect to operational planning, the army remained focused westwards. During the Cold War, the conventional defence of Hokkaido against a Soviet invasion became the JGSDF's primary mission. Surveillance of the straits used by the Soviet Pacific Fleet based in Vladivostok to access the Pacific Ocean, along with coastal surveillance in northern Hokkaido, became part of this mission. The JGSDF's role was substantially enhanced when closure of these straits in wartime was incorporated into national strategic policy in the early 1980s. It was codified in the JGSDF's operational concept of 'Sea Shore Strike', based on 'a scenario for a Soviet landing in Hokkaido', adopted to 'orient its doctrine and procurement strategy'.[2]

The JGSDF has the leading role in coastal surveillance and coastal defence across Hokkaido's northern coastline, from Wakkanai and Cape Soya in the north-west to Nemuro in the north-east, and hosts the Japanese Maritime Self-Defense Force's (JMSDF) shore-based facilities for monitoring submarine passage through the Soya and Nemuro straits. The JGSDF's 301st Coastal Surveillance Unit, based at Wakkanai, has detachments at Maruyama, a hill about 3 kilometres inland from the tip of Cape Soya, and on Rebun Island, about 40 kilometres

---

1   David C. Evans & Mark R. Peattie, *Kaigun: Strategy, Tactics and Technology in the Imperial Japanese Navy, 1887–1941* (Naval Institute Press, Annapolis, Maryland, 1977), p. 149.
2   Euan Graham, *Japan's Sea Lane Security, 1940–2004*, p. 145.

west of Wakkanai, in the north-east part of the Sea of Japan. The 302nd Coastal Surveillance Unit is located at Shibetsu, near Nemuro.[3] These units report to the HQ of the Northern Army at Sapporo in Hokkaido.[4]

The JGSDF has also long maintained Coastal Surveillance Training Centres at Mitsushima and at Kami-tsushima on Tsushima Island in the Korea Strait, at the southern end of the Sea of Japan.[5] These have operational as well as training functions. For example, they were 'mobilised' on 18 December 1998 when South Korean naval forces sunk a North Korean submarine in international waters off northern Kyushu.[6]

The JGSDF's role in coastal defence and control of certain straits was manifested in the decision in the early 1980s to develop a surface-to-surface anti-ship missile, designated the SSM-1 Type-88 and also called the Shibasuta, specifically for the JGSDF. The new system was developed by Mitsubishi Heavy Industries from 1982 to 1987 'to destroy invading ships at landing shore'.[7] The FY 1986–90 Mid-Term Defense Program (MTDP), approved by the Cabinet on 18 September 1985, stated that 54 surface-to-ship guided missiles would be procured 'in order to strengthen the capability to destroy invading forces in the outer seas and coastal waters'; they were to be deployed with three operational units and one training unit.[8] The acquisition of the missiles effectively gave the JGSDF 'an integral role in the defence of the Soya and Tsugaru Straits'.[9]

The FY 1991–95 MTDP, approved by the Cabinet on 20 December 1990, stated that procurement of the SSM-1 would 'be continued' beyond the 54 already authorised, and included funds for another 40 Shibasuta.[10] The JGSDF now has 100 Type-88s. Deployment of the Type-88 began in 1989–90; 16 were operational

---

3　「警戒監視情報の収集態勢（１）：陸上及び海上自衛隊」，　アジア太平洋地域の安全保障環境と地域的な安全保障のための取組，第５回「安全保障と防衛力に関する懇談会」資料，平成１６年６月２９日, ['Maritime Surveillance and Intelligence Collection (1) JGSDF and JMSDF', *Asia-Pacific Security Environment and Measures for Regional Security*, Council on Security and Defense Capabilities, 29 June 2004], at www.kantei.go.jp/jp/singi/ampobouei/dai5/5siryou.pdf

4　「第301沿岸監視隊」, ['301 Coastal Surveillance Unit'], Wikipedia – Japanese, at ja.wikipedia.org/wiki/%E7%AC%AC301%E6%B2%BF%E5%B2%B8%E7%9B%A3%E8%A6%96%E9%9A%8A;　'沿岸監視隊_(陸上自衛隊)' ['Coastal Monitoring Teams (GSDF)'], Wikipedia – Japanese, at ja.wikipedia.org/wiki/%E6%B2%BF%E5%B2%B8%E7%9B%A3%E8%A6%96%E9%9A%8A_(%E9%99%B8%E4%B8%8A%E8%87%AA%E8%A1%9B%E9%9A%8A)

5　「県内自衛隊施設数量の詳細」、長崎平和委員会 ['Details of SDF Facilities in the Nagasaki Prefecture'], *Nagasaki Peace Committee News*, 31 March 2001, at www7b.biglobe.ne.jp/~chi-tan/nsdf002.html

6　*Tokyo Shimbun*, 9 January 1999, in American Embassy, Tokyo, 'Daily Summary of Japanese Press', 13 January 1999.

7　Japan Defense Agency (JDA), *Defense of Japan 1991* (The Japan Times, Tokyo, 1991), p. 250; and 'SSM-1: Shibasuta SSM–1B Type 88, Type 90', at www.deagel.com/Anti-Ship-Missiles/SSM-1_a001943001.aspx.

8　JDA, *Defense of Japan 1987* (The Japan Times, Tokyo, 1987), pp. 109, 298, 301; and JDA, *Defense of Japan 1988* (The Japan Times, Tokyo, 1988), pp. 101–02, 307.

9　Graham, *Japan's Sea Lane Security*, p. 145.

10　JDA, *Defense of Japan 1993* (The Japan Times, Tokyo, 1993), pp. 270, 273, 276.

in 1992, 24 in 1993, and about 50 in 1995–96. It had 60 Type-88s operational in 1996, 80 in 1998, and 100 by 2000–01.[11] The Type-88 missile is 5.1 metres long, 0.35 metres in diameter, weighs 660 kilograms, and carries a 225 kilogram AP-HE warhead. It has a maximum effective range of 180 kilometres, has both an inertial guidance system and an active radar seeker for the terminal phase, and integral electronic counter-countermeasures (ECCM) capability provided by a 'home on jamming' capability.[12] Six missiles are carried on a truck/launcher vehicle.

The JGSDF has six Surface-to-Ship Missile Regiments, each of which has two or three trucks, or 12–18 Type-88 missiles. Three of the regiments are elements of the Northern Army in Hokkaido – the 1st Regiment at Kita-Chitose, the 2nd at Bibai in Surachi Sub-Prefecture, and the 3rd at Kami-Furano in Kamikawa Sub-Prefecture; the 4th is based at Hachinohe with the North-East Army; the 5th is at Kengun in Kumamoto Prefecture in Kyushu, the HQ of the Western Army; and the 6th is at Utsunomiya, in Tochigi Prefecture, north of Tokyo, with the Eastern Army. A detachment of the 301st Communications Company is based with the 3rd Regiment at Kami-Furano to provide direct communications with the JGSDF's 301st Coastal Surveillance Unit at Wakkanai. With units of the 5th Regiment based in Tsushima, the JGSDF is now able to effectively control the Soya, Tsugaru and Tsushima straits.[13]

On 6–7 November 2013, as noted in chapter 2, four Type-88 missiles were deployed to Naha air base in Okinawa and two to Miyako-jima during a large-scale exercise to test Japan's capacity to block foreign vessels from transiting between the East China Sea and the western Pacific through the gap between Okinawa and Miyako-jima. The missiles and two launchers were from the 3rd Regiment at Kami-Furana in Hokkaido.[14]

A successor to the Type-88, initially called the Improved Type-88 or Type-88 (Kai), but now designated the Type-12, has been developed by the Technical Research and Development Institute (TRDI).[15] Funding for procurement of 24

11   International Institute for Strategic Studies (IISS), *The Military Balance* (London), various annual editions.
12   'Military Photos and Videos: Japan – Type-88 Surface-to-Ship Missile (SSM-1)', at www.militaryspot. com/gallery/showphoto.php?photo=433&cat=527&page=1
13   John O'Connell, 'Strategic Implications of the Japanese SSM-1 Cruise Missile', *Journal of Northeast Asian Studies* (Vol. 6, No. 2), Summer 1987, pp. 53–66.
14   'Japan Installing Missiles on Pacific Gateway Islands', at www.taipeitimes.com/News/front/ archives/2013/11/08/2003576391; David C. Isby, 'JGSDF Type 88 Missile Launchers Deployed for Exercise', *IHS Jane's*, 5 November 2013, at www.janes.com/article/29573/jgsdf-type-88-missile-launchers-deployed-for-exercise
15   Department of Guided Weapon Systems, Technical Research and Development Institute (TRDI), at www. mod.go.jp/trdi/en/programs/gm/gm.html

Type-12s was included in the FY 2012 defence budget, with a further 48 in the FY 2013 budget. The first batch is to be deployed with the 5th Regiment at Kumamoto.[16]

On 26 March 2008, the JGSDF's Central Army, headquartered at Itami in Osaka, officially established two coastal surveillance units, focused on the south-western part of the Japan Sea separating North Korea from Honshu. One, named the 13th Reconnaissance Squadron, is located at Izumo, in the northern part of Honshu's Shimane Prefecture, just inland from the Japan Sea and around the closest point to North Korea. It has 130 personnel, as well as 10 light armoured vehicles for scout purposes.[17] The other, called a Mobile Coastal Surveillance Unit, has 50 personnel and is based at Imazu in Shiga Prefecture, north-east of Kyoto.[18] Some of the unit's vehicles were displayed in September 2008, one of which carried a 'wide-range monitoring system' called *Senrigan* (*Clairvoyant*), another contained an 'all-weather surveillance room', and a third carried a new JTPS-P23 'ground radar' system. The vehicles provide high mobility and, when they are positioned for their coastal surveillance mission, the 'sophisticated radar', optical devices and various antenna systems are quickly extendable.[19]

At the beginning of July 2009, it was reported that the JGSDF's Western Army planned to establish a coastal surveillance unit and associated radar facility on Yonaguni Island, the westernmost point of Japan and part of the Sakishima Island group; it is about 110 kilometres from the east coast of Taiwan, and about 170 kilometres south-west of the disputed Senkaku Islands. Its purpose is to monitor the movement of vessels in the area, and, more specifically, to 'clarify the intentions' of Chinese naval deployments in the area. The planned unit consists of 300 personnel, drawn from the augmented 1st Combined Brigade based in Naha, Okinawa, and was to have been deployed at Yonaguni by the end of 2009; the plan was expected to be confirmed in the Mid-Term Defense Build-up Plan for FY 2010–14, then being formulated for approval by the Cabinet later

16 「12式地対艦誘導弾」 ['Type-12 Surface-to-Ship Missile'], Wikipedia – Japanese, at ja.wikipedia.org/wiki/12%E5%BC%8F%E5%9C%B0%E5%AF%BE%E8%89%A6%E8%AA%98%E5%B0%8E%E5%BC%BE; Gordon Arthur, 'New Anti-Ship Missile for Japan's Self Defence Force', 2 September 2013, at www.shephardmedia.com/news/landwarfareintl/new-anti-ship-missile-japans-self-defence-force/
17 沿岸監視隊_(陸上自衛隊)」 ['Coastal Monitoring Teams (GSDF)'], at ja.wikipedia.org/wiki/%E6%B2%BF%E5%B2%B8%E7%9B%A3%E8%A6%96%E9%9A%8A_(%E9%99%B8%E4%B8%8A%E8%87%AA%E8%A1%9B%E9%9A%8A); 「出雲駐屯地」 ['Izumo Garrison'], Wikipedia – Japanese, at ja.wikipedia.org/wiki/%E5%87%BA%E9%9B%B2%E9%A7%90%E5%B1%AF%E5%9C%B0; 'Detailed Report of New Units as at End FY 2007', *Asagumo News*, 3 April 2008, at www.asagumo-news.com/news/200804/080403/08040303.html
18 「今津駐屯地」 ['Imazu Garrison'], Wikipedia – Japanese, at ja.wikipedia.org/wiki/%E4%BB%8A%E6%B4%A5%E9%A7%90%E5%B1%AF%E5%9C%B0
19 「陸上自衛隊　今津駐屯地創立５６周年記念行事(今津駐屯地祭２００８)」,北大路機関 ['56th Anniversary of JGSDF Imazu Detachment', Kitaoji Agency], 24 September 2008, at harunakurama.blog.ocn.ne.jp/kitaooji/2008/09/post_919e.html

in 2009.[20] The Defense Minister Yasukazu Hamada visited Yonaguni on 8 July, the first time a defence chief had visited the island. He said in Yonaguni that: 'I am well aware of the need for defence of the Sakeshima island chain and I plan to consider the matter [of establishing a JGSDF Coastal Surveillance Unit] in the future'.[21]

Although some of the island's 1,600 residents were reportedly opposed to the JGSDF presence, it was welcomed by the majority. Indeed Shukichi Hokama, the mayor of Yonaguni, had visited Hamada in Tokyo on 30 June and requested a JGSDF presence on the island 'to provide defence for the offshore islands, assistance during natural disasters, and help promote the local economy'.[22] In August, the mayor was re-elected against an opponent who was opposed to the JGSDF plan.[23]

The reports about the plan raised concerns in both China and Taiwan. Chinese 'experts' reportedly insisted that China has sovereignty over the Senkaku Islands and that Japan did not appreciate China's security interests; they said that a military presence on Yonaguni could provoke an 'inappropriate chain reaction', and that Japan 'should think twice' about the issue.[24] In Taipei, it was argued that 'Taiwan shields Yonaguni from China', and hence that the planned move was 'aimed at Taiwan rather than China'.[25]

In September 2009, following the election of the Democratic Party government, the new Defense Minister, Toshimi Kitazawa, said that he was 'cautious' about the Yonaguni proposal. He said that 'from the viewpoint of national defense, sending troops to Yonaguni is basically important', but that 'I doubt whether

---

20 'The GSDF Deployment to Yonaguni: Making Border Defence Explicit', *Sankei News*, 5 July 2009, at sankei.jp.msn.com/politics/policy/090705/plc0907050128000-n1.htm; 'Japan May Deploy Troops Near Disputed Islands', *China Post*, 3 July 2009, at www.chinapost.com.tw/asia/japan/2009/07/03/214750/Japan-may.htm; Hisashi Ishimatsu, 'Far Western Isle a Defence Outpost?', *Asahi Shimbun*, 10 July 2009, at www.asahi.com/english/Herald-asahi/TKY200907100075.html

21 Hisashi Ishimatsu, 'Far Western Isle a Defence Outpost?', at www.asahi.com/english/Herald-asahi/TKY200907100075.html

22 ibid; 'Japan Beefs Up Defense Forces in Yonaguni', *The View from Taiwan*, 6 July 2009, at michaelturton.blogspot.com/2009/07/japan-beefs-up-defense-forces-in.html; 'Yonaguni Asks Self Defense Forces for Troop Deployment', *Weekly Japan Update*, 9 July 2009, at two--plus--two.blogspot.com/2009/07/yonaguni-asks-self-defense-forces-for.html

23 'Pro-JGSDF Mayor Wins Reelection', *Weekly Japan Update*, 6 August 2009, at two--plus--two.blogspot.com/2009/08/pro-jsdf-mayor-wins-reelection.html

24 'Chinese Experts Say the Japanese Military Deployment is Close to Sensitive Areas of China', *China Military Report*, 4 July 2009, at wuxinghongqi.blogspot.com/2009/07/chinese-experts-said-deployment-of.html

25 Lai I-chung, 'Yonaguni Plans Raise Questions of Taiwan', *Taipei Times*, 6 July 2009, at www.taipeitimes.com/News/editorials/archives/2009/07/06/2003447948

the matter requires urgency'. He said that it was important 'not to raise security concerns among neighbouring countries', and that 'the plan would be reassessed'.[26]

In July 2010, however, 'senior' Ministry of Defense (MoD) officials said the ministry was still considering the plan, and that it 'envisioned' that 'the coastal monitoring unit to be sent to Yonaguni Island' would 'be modelled' on the JGSDF's No. 301 Coastal Surveillance Unit at Wakkanai and the No. 302 Coastal Surveillance Unit at Shibetsu/Nemuro.[27]

On 11 November 2010, Kitazawa announced that the government had decided to proceed with the proposal, and that 100 troops would initially be stationed on the island to conduct 'surveillance of Chinese naval vessels'. He said that the MoD had requested that 30 million yen (about US$365,000) be included in the FY 2011 budget for 'preparatory research', including site selection. Reports stated that the MoD planned to eventually deploy some 200 personnel to the station.[28]

The MoD's MTDP (FY2011–FY2015), approved by the Cabinet on 17 December 2010, officially endorsed the project. It stated that:

> The GSDF will establish a new coastal surveillance unit, and will begin to form a first-response unit to station in the island areas of southwestern Japan, to gather intelligence, monitor situations, and respond swiftly when incidents occur.[29]

In July 2011, MoD officials gave a presentation to Yonaguni residents concerning the scale, general purpose and construction schedule for the project, as well as the site selection process, which was then nearing finalisation. The residents were still sharply divided.[30] Mayor Hokama said in early 2011 that he hoped the new garrison would bring 'an influx of badly needed jobs and youthful residents, especially if the soldiers come with their families'. Opponents feared that the soldiers would bring 'noise and crime'. They also feared that the project would harm ties between the island and Taiwan. Hokama said that he 'used to

---

26 'Defense Minister Cautious About Deploying GSDF on Westernmost Island', *Kyodo*, 25 September 2009, at www.breitbart.com/article.php?id=D9AU3VE80&show_article=1; 'Japan to Reassess Plan to Deploy Troops on Yonaguni', *NHK News*, 26 September 2009, at www.nhk.or.jp/news/t10015700241000.html#
27 'Beefed-up Okinawa Border Eyed', *Japan Times*, 20 July 2010, at www.japantimes.co.jp/text/nn20100720a5.html; 'Editorial: Why Try to Rock the Boat?', *China Post*, 29 July 2010, at www.chinapost.com.tw/editorial/world-issues/2010/07/29/266563/Why-try.htm
28 'Japan May Place Troops Close to Disputed Islands', *Taipei Times*, 10 November 2010, at www.taipeitimes.com/News/front/archives/2010/11/10/2003488154; 'Japan to Send Troops to Remote Isle Over China Fears', *AFP*, 11 November 2010, at www.rsis.edu.sg/research/RMA_bulletin/RMA%20Bulletin%202410.pdf
29 Ministry of Defense, 'Mid-Term Defense Program (FY2011–FY2015)', 17 December 2010.
30 James Simpson, 'As Plans for Coastal Monitoring Unit Proceed, Yonaguni Residents Raise Voices', 22 August 2011, at jsw.newpacificinstitute.org/?p=7801#comments

be a socialist who opposed the Self-Defense Force's very existence', but that he 'became a base proponent after Chinese ships began appearing in nearby waters a decade or so ago'.[31]

On 21 August 2011, *Mainichi Shimbun* reported that the MoD had selected 15–20 hectares of a 125-hectare farm in the south-west part of the island, then being used for grazing about 60 cows and horses. It was municipal land belonging to Yonaguni Town. It was reported that initial procurement funds were included in the FY 2012 budget, that the project comprised a signals intelligence (SIGINT) facility, optical equipment and a radar system, together with the unit HQ, barracks and a heliport, and that it was scheduled for completion within four years.[32] On 23 August, Kitazawa confirmed at a press conference that 30 million yen was being spent on 'research' on the Yonaguni station in the FY 2011 budget, that initial construction costs would be included in the FY 2012 budget, and that the MoD intended 'to complete the deployment of the coastal monitoring unit by the end of FY 2015'.[33]

On 20 September 2011, 556 people, or more than a third of the island's total population, and about 46 per cent of eligible voters, signed a petition to the mayor opposing the project. A survey in early September found that the number of those opposed had reached 73.3 per cent.[34] In early October, however, the MoD announced that it had requested 1.6 billion yen in the FY 2012 budget to proceed with construction of the station. This included funds to purchase the land from the Yonaguni Town Office and to 'pay compensation to those affected'. The chief-of-staff of the JGSDF, Eiji Kimizuka, said that: 'As the GSDF, we have to upgrade our monitoring functions (in the southern seas) to the same levels as those in Hokkaido'. Hokama said that: 'There are no other ways to revitalize our island'.[35] On 18 November 2011, the MoD provided a briefing for Yonaguni residents in which it explained its plans and 'the reasons behind choosing Yonaguni'.[36]

31   Martin Packler, 'Japanese Isle in Sea of Contention Weighs Fist Versus Open Hand', *New York Times*, 10 February 2011, at www.nytimes.com/2011/02/11/world/asia/11island.html?pagewanted=all

32   'Gov't Eyes Obtaining Land on Southwestern Isle for Coastal Monitoring', *Mainichi Shimbun*, 21 August 2011; 'Japan Mulls Coastal Monitoring Unit in Wake of China's Naval Activity', *Kyodo News*, 21 August 2011, at www.accessmylibrary.com/article-1G1-264916415/japan-mulls-coastal-monitoring.html; Simpson, 'As Plans for Coastal Monitoring Unit Proceed, Yonaguni Residents Raise Voices', at jsw.newpacificinstitute. org/?p=7801#comments

33   'Press Conference by the Defense Minister', Tokyo, 23 August 2011, at www.mod.go.jp/e/ pressconf/2011/08/110823.html

34   Gavan McCormack, 'Yonaguni: Dilemmas of a Frontier Island in the East China Sea', *The Asia-Pacific Journal*, September 2012, at japanfocus.org/-Gavan-McCormack/3837#

35   Kim Soonhi, 'Islanders Split as Ministry Seeks 1.5 Billion Yen to Deploy SDF', *Asahi Shimbun*, 3 October 2011, at ajw.asahi.com/article/behind_news/politics/AJ2011100313047.

36   'Japan to Deploy Forces Near Tiaoytais', *China Post*, 19 November 2011.

In September 2012, the MoD requested 6.2 billion yen for the Yonaguni Coastal Defense facility in its budget request for FY 2013. This included 'the price of facilities and monitoring equipment', as well as 'site preparation works'.[37] The budget statement and pursuant media commentary indicated that the planned JGSDF station will comprise four systems: (i) a 7-element CDAA for HF DF purposes, similar to the one installed for No. 301 Coastal Surveillance Unit at Wakkanai in 2009–10; (ii) VHF/UHF monitoring equipment, such as that operated by No. 301 Coastal Surveillance Unit at Maruyama (and depicted in the MoD's budget statement); (iii) a large UHF monitoring system, such as that operated by No. 301 Coastal Surveillance Unit on Rebun Island (and also depicted in the MoD's budget statement); and, (iv) a mobile radar system.

Planning was again interrupted when, on 20 March 2013, Hokama unexpectedly presented the MoD with a demand for 1 billion yen as a 'nuisance payment' to compensate local landowners, in addition to an annual rent of 15 million yen. The MoD responded a week later, with a spokesman stating that: 'The MoD will continue to negotiate positively with the islanders, but if we do not see any progress, we will have no choice but to review the plan, including whether to deploy the troops on the island'.[38] Press reports said that alternative sites, including Miyako-jima and Ishigaki Island, were being considered.[39] On 20 June, however, the Yonaguni Assembly formally adopted a resolution withdrawing the demand for the 'nuisance payment' and agreeing to the annual rent of 15 million yen for the lease of 'about 214,000 square metres of land'. On 27 June, the MoD and the assembly signed a contract to this effect, with completion of the station still scheduled for the end of FY 2015.[40]

Construction of the new facility began with a ground-breaking ceremony on 19 April 2014. The ceremony was attended by the Minister of Defense, Itsunori Onodera, who said that it was 'a part of our effort to strengthen the surveillance over the southwestern region' and that: 'We are staunchly determined to protect Yonaguni Island, a part of the precious Japanese territory'. Some Yonaguni

---

37 「我が国の防衛と予算, 平成２５年度概算要求の概要」 [Defense Programs and Budget of Japan, Overview of FY 2013 Budget Request], 防衛省[Ministry of Defense], September 2012, p. 5, at www.mod.go.jp/j/yosan/2013/gaisan.pdf; and James Simpson, 'Key Figures from the MoD FY2013 Budget Request', *Japan Security Watch*, 7 September 2012, at jsw.newpacificinstitute.org/?p=10480
38 Paul Kallender, 'Japan–China Island Spat Threatens GSDF Deployment and Much More', *Defense News*, 1 May 2013.
39 'Japan to Give Up Yonaguni Garrison Only 150 km Away from Diaoyu Islands', *Sankei*, 20 March 2013; and 「陸自配備　年１２００～１４００万円で与那国と用地賃貸借」 ['GSDF Deployment: 12–14 Million Yen Yonaguni Site Annual Lease'], *MSN-Sankei News*, 19 June 2013, at sankei.jp.msn.com/politics/news/130619/plc13061900380000-n1.htm
40 'SDF Will Build a New Military Base Only 150 km Away from the Diaoyu Islands', 21 June 2013, at www.best-news.us/news-4707397-SDF-will-build-a-new-military-base-is-only-150-km-away-from-the-Diaoyu-Islands.html; 'Japanese Self-Defense Forces Will be Stationed at Diaoyu Islands to Monitor China', 29 June 2013, at www.best-news.us/news-4773774-Japanese-Self-Defense-Forces-will-be-stationed-at-Diaoyu-islands-nearest-to-monitor-China.html

residents who were opposed to the new station scuffled with MoD officials at the ceremony. Officials reiterated that the unit would become operational in March 2016.[41]

In addition, there have been persistent reports since 2010 that the JMSDF has already deployed a sound surveillance system (SOSUS)-type undersea surveillance system connected to a shore station on Yonaguni.[42]

41   Nobuhiro Kubo, 'Japan to Arm Remote Western Island, Risking More China Tension', *Reuters*, 18 April 2014, at www.reuters.com/article/2014/04/18/us-japan-military-islands-idUSBREA3H05M20140418; 'Local Anger at Japan Island Surveillance Unit', *Aljazeera*, 20 April 2014, at www.aljazeera.com/news/asia-pacific/2014/04/local-anger-at-japan-island-surveillance-unit-201442044145528401.html
42   '中国艦隊通過　外洋進出に懸念　政府「動き注視」' ['Government Concerned to "Watch Movements" of Chinese Fleet Transiting to the Open Ocean'], *Japan Research Center of Military Affairs*, 14 April 2010, at www.kamiura.com/whatsnew/continues_398.html; Kyle Mizokami, 'Yonaguni is Getting a Garrison', *Japan Security Watch*, 10 November 2010, at jsw.newpacificinstitute.org/?p=3116; '中国海军039级等多型潜艇与驱逐舰练对抗攻防' ['US and Japan Work Together to Establish Undersea Listening Network Close to Chinese Submarine Bases'], *Beijing Daily*, 10 July 2013, at dailynews.sina.com/bg/chn/chnmilitary/sinacn/20130710/00164728365.html

5. The Organisation of the JMSDF: The High Command, Fleet Bases and Regional Districts

The Japanese Maritime Self-Defense Force (JMSDF) is commanded by the chief of the Maritime Staff, based at the Ministry of Defense (MoD) HQ at Ichigaya in Tokyo. From 1954 to 2006, he was supported by the powerful Maritime Staff Office (MSO), which was responsible for all aspects of supervision of the JMSDF, which includes the Self-Defense Fleet, five regional district commands (with HQs at Ominato, Yokosuka, Kure, Maizuru and Sasebo), the Air Training Squadron and various support units, such as hospitals and schools, and including operational command as well as administrative, personnel, training and capability acquisition matters (see Fig. 1). In March 2006, in a move to integrate the JMSDF's operational planning and command structures, a new joint staff office was established at the Japan Defense Agency (JDA) HQ at Ichigaya, to which the MSO's operational planning and command functions were transferred; the truncated MSO retained all its other 'force provider' functions.[1] The Basic Intelligence Center which had served the MSO at Ichigaya, correlating and analysing intelligence collected by all the JMSDF's assets, was also transferred to the Defense Intelligence Headquarters (DIH) at Ichigaya in March 2006.

The JMSDF Fleet is headquartered at Yokosuka, on the Uraga Suido (Channel), just inside the entrance to Tokyo Bay, and is charged with defence of all waters around the Japanese archipelago. It commands four escort flotillas (two based in Yokosuka and one each in Sasebo and Maizuru), the JSMDF Fleet Air Force headquartered at Atsugi, two submarine flotillas based at Kure and Yokosuka, two minesweeping flotillas based at Kure and Yokosuka, and the Fleet Training Command at Yokosuka.

The Fleet HQ is supported by an Electronic Intelligence Center (EIC), which processes, correlates and analyses electronic intelligence collected by its EP-3 aircraft, electronic intelligence (ELINT) shore stations and ship-based systems; a Fleet Intelligence Center (FIC), which compiles and analyses intelligence from the various ocean surveillance systems; and an Operational Intelligence Center (OIC), which provides intelligence reports for the operational commanders. The OIC, which had a staff of more than 65 in 2000, also maintains the JMSDF OSIS Evolutionary Development (JOED) workstations.[2]

---

1 Ministry of Defense, *Defense of Japan 2006* (Tokyo, 2006), pp. 148–53, at www.mod.go.jp/e/publ/w_paper/index.html
2 'CV: Senior Systems Security Engineer', at space-careers.com/agency/cvview_7971.html

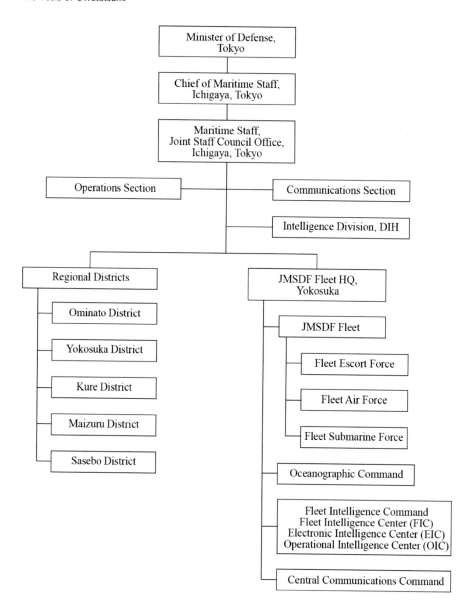

Figure 1. Organisation of the JMSDF

Source: Author's compilation

Also located at the Fleet HQ are the HQs of the Fleet Intelligence Command, which manages and supervises intelligence personnel stationed at shore bases and afloat; the JMSDF Central Communications Command, which provides the communications facilities for the Fleet HQ; and the JMSDF Oceanographic Command, which has important ocean surveillance capabilities.

The Oceanographic Command has an Anti-submarine Intelligence Unit and a Weather Information Unit, and operates two ocean observation stations (at Higashidori and White Beach) with sound surveillance system (SOSUS) arrays, four ocean observation ships, two Surveillance Towed Array Sensor System (SURTASS) acoustic measurement ships, and a cable-laying ship.[3] There were reportedly 10 buildings and about 100 staff engaged in 'submarine detection operations' at the Oceanographic Command's facility at Yokosuka in the 1980s.[4]

Ominato District

The Ominato Regional District is the northernmost of the JMSDF's five districts. The Ominato District Command is headquartered near the Ominato Port, a few kilometres south-west of Mutsu City, on the north-east side of Mutsu Bay, in the north-east corner of Honshu. Naturally protected inside Mutsu Bay, the Ominato base was originally established by the Japanese navy in 1899, during the Meiji era. It was closed after the end of the Second World War, and reopened as the Ominato Guard Corps base in September 1953.[5]

The Ominato District Command has a general responsibility for defence of the waters surrounding Hokkaido Island and the northern part of Aomori prefecture in northern Honshu, including the southern part of the Sea of Okhotsk, the northern part of the Sea of Japan, and the north-western Pacific, with direct responsibility for the Tsugaru Strait between Hokkaido and Honshu.

It commands four escort destroyers, an underwater disposal unit, three minesweepers, three missile patrol boats and an SH-60J helicopter squadron, used for both anti-submarine warfare (ASW) patrol and search and rescue missions. Subordinate bases are situated at Hakodate, where the minesweepers are based, in the south-west corner of Hokkaido, near the western entrance to

---

3   'Oceanographic Command, Yokosuka', at www.soumu.go.jp/kanku/kanto/kanagawa/pdf/kanagawa18_01_07.pdf

4   Jeffrey T. Richelson, *Foreign Intelligence Organizations* (Ballinger, Cambridge, Massachusetts, 1988), p. 261.

5   「大湊地方隊」 ['Ominato District Command'], Wikipedia – Japanese, at ja.wikipedia.org/wiki/%E5%A4%A7%E6%B9%8A%E5%9C%B0%E6%96%B9%E9%9A%8A

the Tsugaru Strait; Yoichi, on the south-western side of Hokkaido, where the patrol boats are based; and Wakkanai, where a minesweeper and patrol boat are often deployed.[6]

The Hakodate base has administrative and logistical responsibility for the JMSDF's listening stations at Matsumae, Matsumae/Shirakami and Tappi Zaki, on the other side of the Tsugaru Strait. The district HQ at Ominato provides administrative and logistical support for the Shimokita-hanto Ocean Observation Station at Higashidori, on the eastern coast of the Shimokita Peninsula.

Yokosuka District

The Yokosuka Regional District Command is headquartered in the large JMSDF Fleet base at Yokosuka, on the south-western side of the entrance to Tokyo Bay. It is responsible for the defence of the central part of the eastern coast of Honshu, from Iwate Prefecture down to Mie Prefecture, with Tokyo Bay in the middle. It was established as a Japan Coast Guard (JCG) maritime patrol station in April 1952, but became the Yokosuka District HQ of the Maritime Safety Force in August 1952. It commands three destroyers, three minesweepers, and an underwater disposal unit. It is also responsible for the management and supervision of the JMSDF's coastal defense station at Kannon Zaki, a few kilometres south of Yokosuka.[7]

Kure District

The Kure Regional District Command is based at Kure, in Hiroshima Prefecture, on the Inland Sea. Really a suburb of Hiroshima City, Kure is one of Japan's largest shipbuilding centres. A navy base was established at Kure in 1886. By the end of the Second World War, it had grown to be one of the Imperial Japanese Navy's largest bases. It was closed in 1945 but reopened as a Maritime Safety Agency (MSA) base in May 1948. It became the JMSDF's Kure District HQ in July 1954, when special warning and surveillance units were also established for the direct defence of the Osaka urban–industrial area.[8]

The Kure District Command is responsible for the defence of the south-western coast of Honshu, from Yamaguchi and Hiroshima on the Setonaikai (Inland Sea)

---

6 ibid.
7 「横須賀地方隊」, ['Yokosuka District Command'], Wikipedia – Japanese, at ja.wikipedia.org/wiki/%E6%A8%AA%E9%A0%88%E8%B3%80%E5%9C%B0%E6%96%B9%E9%9A%8A
8 「呉地方隊」, ['Kure District Command'], Wikipedia – Japanese, at ja.wikipedia.org/wiki/%E5%91%89%E5%9C%B0%E6%96%B9%E9%9A%8A

east to Mie Prefecture, and including Shikoku Island and the south-eastern side of Kyushu. Its principal bases are at Kure, where its three destroyers are home-ported, and at Hanshin, in Kobe, Hyogo Prefecture, just west of Osaka, where three minesweepers are based.

The Hanshin base is responsible for surveillance of the Harima Nada at the eastern end of the Inland Sea and Osako Bay. It maintains the JMSDF's listening station at Mihama, at the tip of the Kii Peninsula, in Wakayama Prefecture, at the southern entrance to Osaka Bay.[9] It also maintains a magnetic measurement station at Kariya, near Awaji, on the north-western side of Osaka Bay.[10]

Maizuru District

The Maizuru Regional District Command is based at Maizuru, in Kyoto Prefecture, and is responsible for defending the central part of the Sea of Japan, from Akita Prefecture in the north-east of Honshu down to Shimane Prefecture, in south-western Honshu. It participated in the search for and subsequent chase of two North Korean 'spy ships' that were found off the Noto Peninsula in March 1999. A detachment of SH-60J Sea Hawk patrol helicopters from the JMSDF's air base at Tateyama in Chiba Prefecture has been deployed to Maizuru since March 2001.[11] The Maizuru District HQ depends on the underwater surveillance stations at Wakkanai, Rebun Island and Matsumae at the northern end of the Sea of Japan, and in the Tsushima Straits at the southern end, to keep it appraised of submarine movements into its area of responsibility.

Sasebo District

The HQ of the Sasebo Regional District Command is located in the Hirase area of Sasebo City, in Nagasaki Prefecture, in the north-western part of Kyushu. It was established in September 1953 as the Sasebo District HQ of the Maritime Safety Force. Its area of responsibility stretches from the southern part of the Sea of Japan, opposite Yamaguchi Prefecture on the northern side of the south-western end of Honshu, down through the Tsushima Straits, and astride the Ryukyu island chain south to the Sakishima island group (around Miyako Island and Ishigaki Island) in Okinawa Prefecture, east of Taiwan. It commands six

---

9   ibid.
10   仮屋磁気測定所, 阪神基地隊, ['Kariya Magnetic Measurement Station', Hanshin Base Group], JMSDF, at www.mod.go.jp/msdf/hanshin/about/kariya/index.html
11   「舞鶴地方隊」 ['Maizuru District Command'], Wikipedia – Japanese, at ja.wikipedia.org/wiki/%E8%88%9E%E9%B6%B4%E5%9C%B0%E6%96%B9%E9%9A%8A

destroyers and three missile patrol boats, as well as three minesweepers based at Shimonoseki in Yamaguchi Prefecture, at the western entrance to the Inland Sea, and another three minesweepers based at Uruma in Okinawa.[12]

The Sasebo District HQ supervises and supports four coastal defence stations equipped with undersea hydrophone arrays and ELINT collection systems. A station at Mutsure-jima, off the western entrance to the Inland Sea, is responsible to the Shimonoseki Base HQ. Two stations on Tsushima Island and another on Iki Island are managed and coordinated by the Tsushima Coastal Defense Group HQ on Tsushima, which is directly subordinate to the Sasebo District HQ.[13] The Sasebo District HQ also maintains a magnetic measurement station, with facilities at Sakibe, on the south-eastern side of the entrance to Sasebo Bay, built in 1976, and at Tategami, on the western side of the Sasebo port area, built in 1986.[14]

JMSDF Radio Communications Stations

The JMSDF's shore-based monitoring stations, and its ASW and ELINT aircraft bases, are connected by a variety of communications systems, including HF radio, microwave relay, satellite communications (Satcom), and optical fibre cables. The hub of the HF radio network comprises the twin transmitting station in Ichihara City and receiving station in Iioka, in Chiba Prefecture. According to a report in May 1984, these stations received data from all of the JMSDF's listening stations, transmitted orders to and received data from the P-3C Orions, and handled the communications with the JMSDF's escort destroyers. Because of the inadequate number of channels in the HF band, however, the shore-based stations were being connected by UHF (microwave relay) systems, with Satcom systems being proposed for the longer term.[15]

The Ichihara Transmitting Station occupies an extensive area next to a golf course in Ichihara City. It has a microwave tower with four dishes, a large HF inverted conical array, strung between six tall masts, a mast with HF and VHF

---

12 「佐世保地方隊」 ['Sasebo District Command'], Wikipedia – Japanese, at ja.wikipedia.org/wiki/%E4%BD%90%E4%B8%96%E4%BF%9D%E5%9C%B0%E6%96%B9%E9%9A%8A

13 ibid; 「下関基地隊」 ['Shimonoseki Base'], Wikipedia – Japanese, at ja.wikipedia.org/wiki/%E4%B8%8B%E9%96%A2%E5%9F%BA%E5%9C%B0%E9%9A%8A; 「対馬防備隊」 ['Tsushima Defense Group Headquarters'], Wikipedia – Japanese, at ja.wikipedia.org/wiki/%E5%AF%BE%E9%A6%AC%E9%98%B2%E5%82%99%E9%9A%8A; 'Tsushima Defense Group Headquarters', at www1.linkclub.or.jp/~chi-tan/tsushimaboubi.html

14 「崎辺地区海上自衛隊　佐世保市崎辺町」, 長崎平和委員会 [MSDF Sakibe District, Nagasaki Peace Committee], at www7b.biglobe.ne.jp/~chi-tan/sakibesdf.html; 「立神地区自衛隊　佐世保市立神町」, 長崎平和委員会 [MSDF Tategami District, Nagasaki Peace Committee], at www7b.biglobe.ne.jp/~chi-tan/tategamisdf.html

15 Taoka Shunji, 'Sea-lane Defence', *Asahi Shimbun*, 1 May 1984.

vertically polarised inverted conical monopoles, two HF rhombic antennas, two large horizontal HF/VHF log-periodic antennas, and a large horizontal curtain antenna.[16]

The Iioka Receiving Station has a microwave tower with two dishes, three large HF horizontal log-spiral omni-directional broadband systems (supported by six radial catenaries and a central mast), a large HF inverted conical system, a mast with both HF and VHF inverted conical monopoles, several other conical monopoles, a large horizontal HF/VHF log-periodic antenna, and a large TCI Model 524 wide-aperture Super High-gain log-periodic directional HF horizontal curtain antenna.[17] High-resolution Google Earth imagery also shows six satellite communications dishes, three about 8 metres in diameter and three about 5 metres in diameter, next to the receiver building at the south-eastern part of the facility.

The JMSDF also maintains two adjacent transmitting stations at Uenohara and Tateyama, in Tateyama City in Chiba.[18] Tateyama is the home base of the JMSDF's Fleet Air Wing 21, which has two squadrons of SH-60J Sea Hawk maritime patrol and ASW helicopters. The Tateyama transmitters are used for communications with the other JMSDF air bases used by its maritime patrol and ASW aircraft, such as the Fleet Air Force HQ at Atsugi, the EP-3C base at Iwakuni, and the P-3C base at Hachinohe, as well as with both aircraft and ships.

The JMSDF's central communications command at Yokosuka has an attached transmitting and receiving station. It has a tall steel lattice tower with two microwave dishes mounted near the top and at least eight VHF and UHF antennas on the top, as well as a HF doublet strung between two masts nearby, which is used for HF reception. A separate HF transmitting station is maintained at Chiyogasaki, on the Miura peninsula, south of Yokosuka. It has several large HF arrays and a mast with both HF and VHF inverted conical antennas.[19]

In the mid-1990s, the JMSDF also built a pair of transmitting and receiving stations at Kushira and Nejime in Kagoshima Prefecture, in the southernmost part of Kyushu, which provide connectivity with the Yokosuka and Iioka/Ichihara

---

16　「海上自衛隊　市原送信所」，アンテナの見える風景 ['JMSDF Ichihara Transmitting Station', *Landscapes with a View of the Antennas*], at home.p04.itscom.net/yama/Ichihara/Icihara.htm
17　「海上自衛隊　飯岡受信所」，アンテナの見える風景 ['JMSDF Iioka Receiving Station', *Landscapes with a View of the Antennas*], at home.p04.itscom.net/yama/Iioka/Iioka.htm
18　「海上自衛隊　上野原送信所」,アンテナの見える風景 ['JMSDF Uenohara Transmitting Station', *Landscapes with a View of the Antennas*], at home.p04.itscom.net/yama/Uenohara/Uenohara.htm; 「海上自衛隊　館山航空基地」，アンテナの見える風景 ['JMSDF Tateyama Transmitting Station', *Landscapes with a View of the Antennas*], at home.p04.itscom.net/yama/Tateyama_kichi/Tateyama.htm
19　「海上自衛隊　横須賀基地　システム通信隊 (受信所・ 通信所))，　アンテナの見える風景 ['JMSDF Yokosuka Base, System Communications Unit', *Landscapes with a View of the Antennas*], at home.p04.itscom.net/Yokosuka_kichi/Yokosuka_kichi.htm; 「海上自衛隊　千代ヶ崎送信所」，アンテナの見える風景 ['JMSDF Chiyogasaki Transmitting Station', *Landscapes with a View of the Antennas*], at home.p04.itscom.net/yama/Chiyogasaki/Chiyogasaki.htm

stations, and extend the coverage of the JMSDF's HF radio communications thousands of kilometres to the south and south-east. The Kushira Transmitting Station has a microwave tower with a single dish, a large horizontal HF/VHF log-periodic antenna, a large HF conical monopole antenna, and a large triangular HF wire array strung between three tall towers.[20] The Nejime Receiving Station has a tall HF conical monopole, an inverted conical HF array, a large horizontal HF/VHF log-periodic antenna, a HF log-spiral antenna, and a large HF array strung between tall towers.[21]

---

20 「海上自衛隊　串良送信所 ['JMSDF Kushira Transmitting Station', *Landscapes with a View of the Antennas*], September 2009, at home.p04.itscom.net/yama/Kushira/Kushira.htm
21 「海上自衛隊　根占受信所」，アンテナの見える風景 ['JMSDF Nejime Receiving Station', *Landscapes with a View of the Antennas*], September 2009, at home.p04.itscom.net/yama/Nejime/Nejime.htm

6. Japanese Undersea Surveillance Systems, 1920–45

The Japanese navy began research on hydrophones in 1920, initially experimenting with foreign models, although it 'failed to produce a workable copy'.[1] In the early 1930s, after further foreign purchases, it developed systems for installation aboard ships as well as on the sea bottom. The first ship-borne systems, the models 93 and 0, were based on the US MV-type hydrophone, which was imported in 1930; they were deployed aboard all Imperial Japanese Navy (IJN) battleships and destroyers until being superseded in 1943. Research and development was primarily undertaken by the Acoustic Department of the Second Naval Institute at Numazu, on the coast of Shizuoka Prefecture, about 130 kilometres south-west of Tokyo; it was destroyed by a US firebombing air raid in July 1945.[2]

The sea-bottom types could be used only in relatively shallow waters, but were useful for detection of submarine traffic in some of the Japanese straits and for harbour defence. By around 1937, 'coastal hydrophones' had been laid in the Tsugaru and Shimonoseki straits, both of which are narrow and shallow. It was reckoned that those in the Tsugaru Strait 'could give ample warning of the appearance of a hostile submarine'; however, the hydrophone detection in the Shimonoseki (or Kanmon) Strait, between Honshu and Kyushu, would have been 'imperfect … due to domestic [shipping] traffic in these waters'.[3]

The first sea-bottom hydrophone system designed for harbour protection was the Type K, developed in 1935–36. It 'was not used in practice', however, and it could only be used in shallow waters of up to 40 metres: 'the bearing accuracy was poor, and binaural reception made it difficult to train operators'.[4] (Binaural reception required headphones with microphone recorders connected to the ear canals of the listener.)

1   Mark P. Parillo, *The Japanese Merchant Marine in World War II* (Naval Institute Press, Annapolis, Maryland, 1993), pp. 108–09.
2   US Naval Technical Mission to Japan, 'Intelligence Targets Japan: Japanese Sonar and Asdic', 14 December 1945, pp. 6, 57, at www.fischer-tropsch.org/primary_documents/gvt_reports/USNAVY/USNTMJ%20 Reports/USNTMJ_toc.htm; Evans & Peattie, *Kaigun*, p. 440.
3   Albert Parry & Alexander Kiralfy, 'Soviet Submarines in the Far East', *Public Affairs* (Vol. 10, No. 1), March 1937, pp. 32–33.
4   US Naval Technical Mission to Japan, 'Intelligence Targets Japan: Japanese Electronic Harbor Protection Equipment', 14 February 1946, pp. 17–18, at www.fischer-tropsch.org/primary_documents/gvt_reports/ USNAVY/USNTMJ%20Reports/USNTMJ_toc.htm

Two types of sea-bottom hydrophone arrays were developed for harbour defence in 1936–37, called types 97 and 1. The Type 1 had 10 microphones, arrayed in a circle just 1 metre in diameter; it had a frequency range of 500 to 3,500 hertz, and was able to determine the direction of sounds to an accuracy of about 10°.[5]

The Type 97 hydrophone system, which came in four successive models (0, 1, 2 and 3), was produced in large numbers from 1937 to 1942. By 1944, 80 Type 97 models had been installed. The Model 1 could be used to a depth of up to 80 metres, the Model 2 up to 150 metres, and the Model 3 up to 250 metres. The Type 97 consisted of 13 microphones arranged in a 3-metre diameter circle, operated in the frequency range from 500 to 2,500 hertz, and provided an accuracy of about 5°. A postwar report by the US Navy reckoned that at the beginning of the war, the system could detect a US submarine running at 5 knots out to a range of about 5 kilometres. Another report stated that, later in the war, it could detect larger submarines travelling at 5 knots out to a range of about 10 kilometres, but against smaller submarines moving at under 3 knots, its range was less than a kilometre. The 'sonic bearing evaluators' for the Type 97s were manufactured by Oki Denki (Oki Electric Industry Company) and Nippon Denki Manufacturing companies.[6]

The Type 97 hydrophones had a major weakness. The noise made by schools of 'snapping shrimp' feeding in the harbours obfuscated the sound of submarines. Indeed, 'sometimes the noise of ships directly over the underwater phones was drowned out completely'. It was revealed after the war that US submarines had used the shrimp noise 'as a screen to hide from' the hydrophone detectors 'many' times when entering Japanese harbours in 1944–45. The Japanese navy 'took more than a year to trace troubles in their own sound detectors to noisy fish', and 'not until 1944 did their biologists undertake a survey of these fish'. However, 'the biologists were bombed out of every station they set up for this purpose'.[7]

In addition to the hydrophones, the IJN also developed sea-bottom magnetic loop detectors for harbour defence. The Type 2 Model 1 system, produced in 1942, consisted of two oval loops, from about 1,500 metres to 3,000 metres in length and from 200 to 300 metres wide, depending on the local geography.

---

5 US Naval Technical Mission to Japan, 'Japanese Sonar and Asdic', 14 December 1945, pp. 12, 33, at www.fischer-tropsch.org/primary_documents/gvt_reports/USNAVY/USNTMJ%20Reports/USNTMJ_toc.htm
6 Norman Friedman, *U.S. Submarines Through 1945: An Illustrated Design History* (Naval Institute Press, Annapolis, Maryland, 1995), p. 247; US Naval Technical Mission to Japan, 'Japanese Sonar and Asdic', 14 December 1945, pp. 12, 33, at www.fischer-tropsch.org/primary_documents/gvt_reports/USNAVY/USNTMJ%20Reports/USNTMJ_toc.htm; US Naval Technical Mission to Japan, 'Japanese Electronic Harbor Protection Equipment', 14 February 1946, pp. 11, 17–18, 27, 31, at www.fischer-tropsch.org/primary_documents/gvt_reports/USNAVY/USNTMJ%20Reports/USNTMJ_toc.htm
7 'Shrimp Aided Submarines: Yankee U-boats Used Snapping Sounds to Foil Jap Detectors', *Reading Eagle*, 16 March 1947, at news.google.com/newspapers?nid=1955&dat=19470316&id=clgrAAAAIBAJ&sjid=-pwFAAAAIBAJ&pg=4836,4206655

Ships or submarines passing overhead affected the magnetic fields in the area, which were monitored by galvanometers in the shore-based guard stations.[8] The Magnetic Detection Department of the Second Naval Research Institute conducted research on 'magnetic apparatus' for submarine detection at a facility at Hayama, near Yokosuka, in Kanagawa Prefecture.[9]

The combination of Type 97 hydrophones and Type 2 Model 1 magnetic loop detectors were used to protect Tokyo Bay and all of the entrances to Setonaikai (Inland Sea). The standard practice was to lay a network of Type 93 contact mines at the mouth of the harbour or strait (with 'approximate provisions for safety channels'), with a Type 2 Model 1 or Model 4 magnetic loop detector laid inside the minefield, and then 'a number of Type 97 hydrophones', with a last line of Type 92 controlled mines.[10]

In the case of the Inland Sea, the narrow Shimonoseki (or Kanmon) Strait at the western entrance was easily covered, while Awaji Island blocked the south-eastern entrance. The Bungo Strait, however, between Kyushu and Shikoku Islands and providing the south-western entrance to the Inland Sea, was mostly wider and deeper; at its narrowest part, between Sada-misaki and Saganoseki, there is a 5-knot tidal current which 'masked any received signal'. According to a postwar technical assessment by the US Navy, the Bungo Strait was 'the major harbour defence problem in Japan'.[11] It was the responsibility of the IJN Defense Unit at Saeki, on the Kyushu side; it commanded 11 guard stations (Bobi-sho) located on both sides of the Strait (at Saeki, Seri Zaki, Hiburi, Yura, Hodo, Oshima, Tsurumi-zaki, Komo, Ukuru, Oki and Fuka-shima), which had a total of 45 Type 97 hydrophones and seven Type 2 Model 1 magnetic loop detectors (see Map 2). The Type 97 hydrophone arrays controlled from Oshima on the Kyushu side and Yura on the Shikoku side came together in the middle of the Strait, forming a single field; it 'was of such a width that it took a ship travelling at two knots 30 minutes to traverse it'.[12] The arrays controlled from Hodo and Hiburi formed a similar field about 10 kilometres inside the Oshima-Yura field. At the outer entrance, hydrophones controlled from Seri Zaki and

8   US Naval Technical Mission to Japan, 'Japanese Electronic Harbor Protection Equipment', 14 February 1946, pp. 13–14, at www.fischer-tropsch.org/primary_documents/gvt_reports/USNAVY/USNTMJ%20 Reports/USNTMJ_toc.htm

9   US Naval Technical Mission to Japan, 'Intelligence Targets Japan: Japanese Electronics – General', 29 December 1945, p. 8, at www.fischer-tropsch.org/primary_documents/gvt_reports/USNAVY/USNTMJ%20 Reports/USNTMJ_toc.htm

10   US Naval Technical Mission to Japan, 'Japanese Electronic Harbor Protection Equipment', 14 February 1946, p. 7, at www.fischer-tropsch.org/primary_documents/gvt_reports/USNAVY/USNTMJ%20Reports/ USNTMJ_toc.htm

11   ibid.

12   ibid, pp. 7–10.

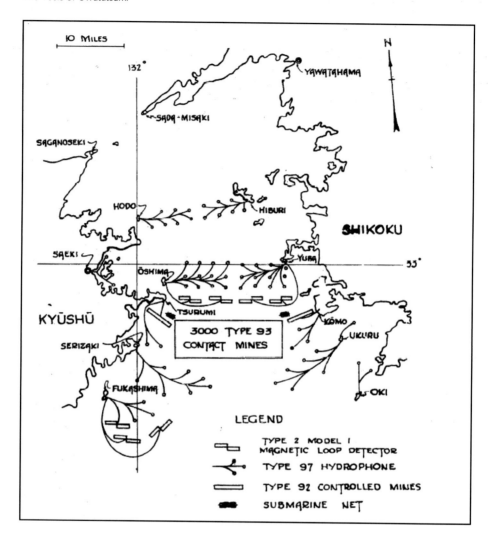

Map 2. Plan of Imperial Japanese Navy (IJN) defences of the Bungo Channel between Kyushu and Shikoku, 1945

Source: US Naval Technical Mission to Japan, 'Japanese Electronic Harbor Protection Equipment', February 1946, p. 8, at www.fischer-tropsch.org/primary_documents/gvt_reports/USNAVY/USNTMJ%20Reports/USNTMJ-200B-0692-0725%20Report%20E-26

Fuka-shima extended from the south-western side, and arrays controlled from Komo, Ukuru and Oki extended from the south-eastern side. The system was supposed to work as follows:

> If, for example, an incoming target was detected by the Seri Zaki Guard Station hydrophones, the Defense Unit at Saeki and the Guard Station at Tsurumi were to be immediately informed by radio … The Guard Station at Tsurumi was expected to be able to track the target in on

its hydrophones and destroy it when it passed through the Type 92 controlled mine field. If by some chance a target succeeded in passing through either the Type 92 or Type 93 mines, it was to be further tracked by the magnetic loops and hydrophones at Oshima, Yura, Hodo and Hiburi, and all information transmitted to the Defense Unit [at Saeki] which plotted all incoming data … Sub-chasers and patrol boats were [then] to be dispatched to drop depth charges.[13]

Three hydrophone fields were connected to shore stations on the Tsushima Islands to monitor submarine traffic through the Korea/Tsushima Strait and the southern entrance of the Sea of Japan (see Map 3). The shore stations were located on Uni-shima, the small island just off the northern point of the northern part of Tsushima Island, from which hydrophone arrays could be extended both westwards towards the Korean Peninsula and eastwards towards south-western Honshu; Go-saki, on the north-western point of the southern part of Tsushima, from which hydrophone arrays extended westwards; and at Ko-saki, at the southern point of the southern part of Tsushima Island, from which arrays again extended both westwards and eastwards.[14]

---

13   ibid, p. 7.
14   US Naval Technical Mission to Japan, 'Intelligence Targets Japan: Defenses of Tsushima and Entrance to Sea of Japan', 11 January 1946, at www.fischer-tropsch.org/primary_documents/gvt_reports/USNAVY/ USNTMJ%20Reports/USNTMJ_toc.htm

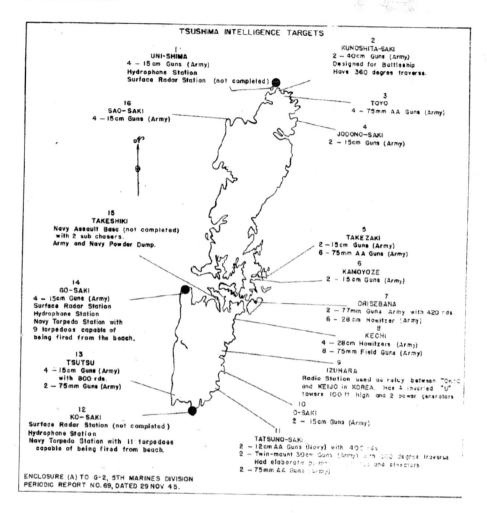

Map 3. IJN defences of Tsushima Island, 1945

Source: Adapted from US Naval Technical Mission to Japan, 'Defenses of Tsushima and Entrance to Sea of Japan', January 1946, p. 13, at www.fischer-tropsch.org/primary_documents/gvt_reports/USNAVY/ USNTMJ%20Reports/USNTMJ-200F-0725-0738%20Report%20O-55%20N

7. Technical Developments since 1945

The Japanese Maritime Self-Defense Force (JMSDF) installed its so-called 'first generation' hydrophone system at several of its new coastal defence stations in the mid- and late 1950s. This used drum-shaped hydrophones, 4 metres in diameter and 2.5 metres high, with a low discrimination capability.[1] The upward-looking arrays were mainly useful for harbour defence, but they could also be strung across key narrow straits. The coastal defence stations established in this period were located at Kannon Zaki, across the Uraga Channel leading into Tokyo Bay; Awaji, on the north-western side of Osaka Bay; Mutsure-jima, astride the entrance to the Kanmon Strait; and at Kogozaki, at the entrance to Sasebo Bay.

In the late 1960s and 1970s, the initial hydrophone system was replaced and supplemented by a total of 19 LQO-3 arrays, produced in Japan. The LQO-3 was designed for use across relatively shallow and narrow straits, especially the Tsugaru and Tsushima straits, with widths ranging from about 20 kilometres to about 50 kilometres. Five sets were installed in the Tsushima Straits, the first two of which were installed (at Kami-tsushima and Iki Island) in 1968, and another (at Shimo-tsushima) in 1972.[2] Another five sets were also installed, beginning in 1968, on the bottom of the Tsugaru Strait, connected to shore stations at Matsumae and Tappi Zaki, on the northern and southern sides of the western entrance to the strait, and at Hachinohe, which monitored submarines passing from the eastern end of the Tsugaru Strait into the Pacific and approaching the strait from the Pacific. A single LQO-3 array was laid in the Soya Strait.[3]

The LQO-3 arrays were upgraded to LQO-3A systems in the early 1980s. It has been suggested that the system had a 70 per cent probability of detecting a submarine travelling at 6 knots at a range of 1,000 yards, and a 15 per cent probability at 3,000 yards, which 'would be entirely acceptable in a barrier, as opposed to an open-ocean, tracking system'.[4]

These stations are also equipped with microwave antennas for transmission of the acoustic recordings, HF and VHF poles, and VHF/UHF/SHF antennas

---

1 Taoka Shunji, 'Sea-lane Defence', *Asahi Shimbun*, 1 May 1984.
2 Friedman, *Naval Institute Guide*, p. 21; Naoaki Usui, 'Japan Plans to Bolster Already Formidable ASW Ability', *Defense News*, 24 June 1991, p. 14; 'Sea-bottom Cable-laying Ship Operating Offshore', in *Asahi Shimbun*, 17 June 1984.
3 Richelson, *Foreign Intelligence Organizations*, p. 261; Naoaki Usui, 'Japan Plans to Bolster Already Formidable ASW Ability', p. 14.
4 Friedman, *Naval Institute Guide*, p. 21.

for electronic intelligence (ELINT) collection to support the development of electronic support measures (ESM) systems and electronic warfare (EW) tactics. Many of them also have marine surveillance radars.

Another sort of SOSUS (sound surveillance system), designed for open-ocean operations, was developed in the late 1960s and installed at one or more stations at the beginning of the 1970s. It was the subject of dogged questioning of the head of the Japan Defense Agency (JDA), Ezaki Masumi, by a Japanese Communist Party representative, Watanabe Takeshi, in the Diet on 18 December 1971. In 1970–71, the JMSDF received three long cables manufactured by the Ocean Company Ltd (OCC) in Yokohama, together with amplifiers designed by the US Navy. The cables incorporated new techniques developed in the United States during production of the first transatlantic telephone cables, including techniques for the emplacement of the cables and booster stations at extreme ocean depths. The cables were 200 kilometres (110 nautical miles), 330 kilometres (180 nautical miles) and 1,150 kilometres (620 nautical miles) in length, were relatively thick, and most suitable for deep-sea use. The repeaters/amplifiers were on average about 70 kilometres (38.7 nautical miles) apart. The cables were delivered to the JMSDF's District HQ at Ominato, for deployment by the *Tsugaru* cable-laying ship.[5] There has been considerable speculation that at least the longest one was installed off the Matsumae Coastal Defense Station.[6] (It is only about 500 kilometres from Matsumae directly west to the Russian coast; a cable of this length could only be laid in a southerly direction, towards the Korean Peninsula and the Tsushima Strait.)

Development of the LQO-4, a lower frequency, longer range system than the LQO-3 or LQO-3A, began in the 1970s. It was designed by the Technical Research and Development Institute's (TRDI) 5th Research Center together with Oki Denki (Oki Electric Industry Company). It was reported in May 1984 that development of the system was scheduled for completion in FY 1985, with initial deployment in 1986.[7] It 'initially coordinated operations of P–2J patrol aircraft'.[8]

In February 1985, *Sekai* magazine reported that installation of LQO-4 systems was proceeding apace. It said that the LQO-3 variants at Cape Shirakami and Tappi Zaki on the northern and southern sides of the western entrance to the

5   67th Diet, Special Committee on Okinawa and the Northern Problem, 18 December 1971, at kokkai.ndl.go.jp/SENTAKU/sangiin/067/1650/06712281650001c.html
6   『北海度のC3I基地に見る新たな福強と変化』、松井愈　　　（著者）、1993年日本平和会国際会議、C3I分科会・18th　全道基地闘争活動者会議（93・10）[Matsui Masaru, 'Looking at New Developments and Changes in Hokkaido C³I Bases, Japan Peace Committee International Conference, C3I Sub-committee; and 18th National Base Struggle Activists Conference (October 1993)', Hokkaido Peace Committee Study Document No. 26, 8–1994], p. 5.
7   Taoka Shunji, 'Sea-lane Defence'.
8   Friedman, *Naval Institute Guide*, p. 21.

Tsugaru Strait had already been replaced by 'new model LQO-4s', and that 'seven LQO-4s are deployed in the Korean and Tsushima Straits', connected to the shore stations at Kami-tsushima, Shimo-tsushima and Iki Island.[9]

The geography of the Sea of Japan is favourable to fixed-bottom sonar operations. Except for the Yamato Seamount at the centre, the bottom of the sea is fairly flat. The straits leading into it – i.e., the Soya, Tsugaru, Tsushima and Shimonoseki Straits – are narrow and mainly shallower than 100 metres, with accessible shorelines for installation of the hydrophone terminals.[10]

A survey of JMSDF contracts for electronic systems since the early 2000s indicates that the LQO-4 was the principal hydrophone system in service until around 2007. There were frequent contracts for components as well as maintenance and repair of LQO-4 systems. On 13 September 2006, for example, Oki Denki's Defense Systems Division received a contract worth 94,132,500 yen for the supply of 8,301 rolls of recording paper for LQO-4 systems. Delivery was due on 31 May 2007.[11] In addition, three contracts were awarded to a variant of the LQO-4, the LQO-4B-1L in 2007–09 (viz: 23 October 2007, 8 October 2008 and 7 October 2009).[12] Since 2007, however, the majority of contracts concerning fixed hydrophone systems have been for LQO-5s (as reported by the Ministry of Defense (MoD) on 23 October 2007, 8 October 2008, 7 October 2009, 8 October 2010, 19 November 2011 and 16 November 2012). There is also a system, the LQO-6, for which a contract was awarded on 7 October 2009.[13]

9 'White Paper: Nuclear War and the Self-Defense Forces', *Sekai*, February 1985, pp. 74–139, in Foreign Broadcast Information Service (FBIS), *Japan Report*, (JPRS–JAR–85–013), 9 May 1985, at www.dtic.mil/cgi-bin/GetTRDoc?Location=U2&doc=GetTRDoc.pdf&AD=ADA349828
10 Richard Deacon, *A History of the Japanese Secret Service* (Frederick Muller, London, 1982), pp. 243–44; Hideo Sekino, 'Japan and Her Maritime Defense', *US Naval Institute Proceedings* (Vol. 97, No. 819), May 1971, pp. 105, 120.
11 「平成18年度 9月期 随意契約一覧表」海上自衛隊艦船補給処管理部長, 市川 順, 神奈川県横須賀市田浦港町無番地。['List of Negotiated Contracts for Period 24 September 2006', General Manager, MSDF Ship Depot, Tauriminato, Yokosuka, Kanagawa Prefecture], Item 33, at www.mod.go.jp/msdf/bukei/yd/nyuusatsu/200609.pdf
12 「海幕公示第3 号、 19．10．12、一部訂正19．10．23. 自衛艦のとう載武器等の検査・ 修理工事の契約希望者募集要項」、防衛書, ['Sea Acts, Public Notice No. 3, 12 October 2007, with Corrections 23 October 2007. Guidelines for Applicants for Construction Contracts, such as Inspection and Repair of MSDF Ship-mounted Weapons', Ministry of Defense], at www.mod.go.jp/msdf/bukei/m0/nyuusatsu/K-19-2020-0003.pdf; 「艦船の検査・ 修理等工事の契約希望者募集要項」、海幕公示第、 海幕公示第3号 20．10．8、防衛省, ['Guidelines for Applicants for Construction Contracts, such as Inspection and Repair of Vessels', Sea Acts, Public Notice No. 3, 8 October 2008. Ministry of Defense], at www.mod.go.jp/msdf/bukei/t1/nyuusatsu/K-20-0000-0003.pdf; 「艦船の検査・ 修理等工事の契約希望者募集要項」、海幕公示第、 海幕公示第3号 21．10．7、防衛省 ['Guidelines for Applicants for Construction Contracts, such as Inspection and Repair of Vessels', Sea Acts, Public Notice No. 3, 7 October 2009. Ministry of Defense], at www.mod.go.jp/msdf/bukei/d0/nyuusatsu/K-21-2610-0043.pdf
13 「艦船の検査・ 修理等工事の契約希望者募集要項」, 海幕公示第、 海幕公示第3号 21．10．7、防衛省 ['Guidelines for Applicants for Construction Contracts, such as Inspection and Repair of Vessels', Sea Acts, Public Notice No. 3, 7 October 2009. Ministry of Defense], Item 239, at www.mod.go.jp/msdf/bukei/d0/nyuusatsu/K-21-2610-0043.pdf

Since the 1940s, the main company involved in the design and production of hydrophones has been Oki Denki. During the Second World War, it manufactured key parts of the Type 97 hydrophones, including the sonic bearing evaluator and the 'maximum sensitivity phasing mechanism'.[14] It has played major roles in the development of all successive LQO systems, including the current LQO-4 and LQO-5 systems. As the MoD explained with respect to the LQO-4 in 2006, Oki Denki 'is the manufacturer of this device' and is the only company 'having the equipment and technology that can guarantee the quality [required for LQO-4 components]'.[15]

Over the past couple of decades, Oki Denki technicians and engineers have been at the forefront of new technical developments. For example, they have constructed hydrophones with porous piezoelectric ceramics, significantly reducing vibrational noise, and hence improving sensitivity compared to non-porous hydrophones;[16] and they have designed an advanced SSBL (super short baseline) acoustic reference system, using a planar hydrophone array consisting of many hydrophone elements for estimating directions, ranges and positions of noise sources.[17] They have made particularly rapid advances with optical fibre hydrophones, obtaining higher sensitivity than that available with piezoelectric sensors.[18] For example, they have recently patented a design for optical fibre hydrophones in which the fibre is coiled around an elastic cylinder, hence enabling the hydrophone to resist high water pressure but retain high sensitivity.[19] They have experimented with optical fibre hydrophones which use fibre Bragg gratings (FBGs) to maintain signal strength in interferometric

14 US Naval Technical Mission to Japan, 'Japanese Electronic Harbor Protection Equipment', 14 February 1946, p. 11, at www.fischer-tropsch.org/primary_documents/gvt_reports/USNAVY/USNTMJ%20Reports/USNTMJ_toc.htm
15 「平成18年度9月期　随意契約一覧表」海上自衛隊艦船補給処管理部長, 市川 順, 神奈川県横須賀市田浦港町無番地。['List of Negotiated Contracts for Period 24 September 2006'], Item 33, at www.mod.go.jp/msdf/bukei/yd/nyuusatsu/200609.pdf
16 Toru Arai, Kazutoshi Ayusawa, Housaki Sato, Tetsuji Miyato, Kazutami Kawamura & Keiichi Kobayashi, 'Properties of Hydrophone with Porous Piezoelectric Ceramics', Japanese Journal of Applied Physics (Vol. 30), 1991, pp. 2253–55.
17 Masao Igarashi & Kazuhiko Nitadori, 'An Advanced SSBL-Acoustic Reference System Using a Planar Hydrophone Array', Electronics and Communications in Japan (Part 1: Communications) (Vol. 65, No. 3), 1982, pp. 1–9.
18 Hiroshi Kamata, 'Realizing Dreams – Yesterday, Today, Tomorrow – An Acoustic/Environmental Sensing Technology Based on Optical Fiber Sensors', Oki Technical Review (No. 189), April 2002, pp. 43–47, at citeseerx.ist.psu.edu/viewdoc/download?doi=10.1.1.197.1088&rep=rep1&type=pdf
19 Saijo Kenji, Ogawara Chiaki, Shimamura Hideki, Sato Ryotaku, Minami Makoto & Tadokoro Yasuaki, 'Optical Fiber Hydrophone Having High Water Pressure Resistance', Patent Number JP2012068087, 5 April 2012, at old.qpat.com/RenderStaticFirstPage?XPN=TCpRzetWHTd7fYsXyd3avbmsLuw/R4oY%20QgpgFzVRnM=

designs,[20] and they have designed miniaturised optical fibre hydrophone arrays using Fabry-Perot interferometers that can operate in deep sea environments and which can easily be mass produced.[21]

Together with the advances in hydrophone technology, Japan has also made enormous progress in signal processing capabilities, whereby acoustic signatures are extracted from background noises. According to reports in the late 1980s, for example, the Japanese acoustic systems were frequently unable to determine the nationality, let alone the identity of individual submarines, by their sound signatures. Since the 1990s, however, Japan has emerged as second only to the United States with respect to military applications of digital acoustic signal processing technologies.

Magnetic Detection Systems

In addition to the various hydrophone arrays, the JMSDF has also developed a variety of magnetic anomaly detection (MAD) systems for both harbour defence and monitoring submarine passage through key straits, which operate in conjunction with the sea-bottom sonar systems. During the Second World War, 'magnetic loop' detection systems were generally installed at all major harbours for anti-submarine protection.[22] For example, Type 2 Model 1 and Type 2 Model 4 magnetic loop systems were used together with Type 97 hydrophones to protect Tokyo Bay and the entrances to the Inland Sea. In the case of the Bungo Strait, seven Model 1 systems were installed on the sea bottom, three off Fuka-Shima at the south-western side of the outer entrance and four across the strait from Oshima to Yura on the outer side of their Type 97 hydrophone field.[23]

Similar magnetic detection systems were installed in the mid- and late 1950s at several of the new coastal defence stations that are responsible for the defence of

20   Kenji Saijyou, Chiaki Okawara, Tomonao Okuyama, Yasuyuki Nakajima & Ryotaku Sato, 'Fiber Bragg Grating Hydrophone with Polarization-maintaining Fiber for Mitigation of Polarization-induced Fading', *Acoustical Science and Technology* (Vol. 33, No. 4), 2012, pp. 239–46.
21   Satou Riyoutaku & Koji Dobashi, 'Optical Fiber Hydrophone', Patent Number JP3160092, 16 February 2001, at www.sumobrain.com/patents/jp/Optical-fiber-hydrophone/JP3160092.html; Hiroshi Asanuma, Satoshi Hashimoto, Shin-ichi Tano, Sho-ichi Takashima, Mitsutomo Nishizawa, Hiroaki Niitsuma & Yugo Shindo, 'Development of Fiber-optical Microsensors for Geophysical Use', July 2003, at niweb.kankyo.tohoku. ac.jp/PDF/SSC2003_Asanuma.pdf; Hiroshi Asanuma, Mitsuyuki Tanaka, Hiroaki Niitsuma & Ryotaku Sato, 'Development of an Optical Micro Hydrophone for Mass Production', *Society of Exploration Geophysicists*, October 2006, at www.onepetro.org/mslib/servlet/onepetropreview?id=SEG-2006-0436
22   US Naval Technical Mission to Japan, 'Intelligence Targets Japan: Japanese Anti-Submarine Warfare', 8 February 1946, p. 9, at www.fischer-tropsch.org/primary_documents/gvt_reports/USNAVY/USNTMJ%20 Reports/USNTMJ-200I-0244-0309%20Report%20S-24.pdf
23   US Naval Technical Mission to Japan, 'Japanese Electronic Harbor Protection Equipment', 14 February 1946, pp. 7–8, 10, at www.fischer-tropsch.org/primary_documents/gvt_reports/USNAVY/USNTMJ%20 Reports/USNTMJ_toc.htm

important harbours. It is likely that these included the stations at Kannon Zaki (Tokyo Bay), Awaji (Osaka Bay), Mutsure-jima (Kanmon Strait) and Kogozaki (Sasebo Bay).

Magnetic measurement stations are currently maintained inside Osaka Bay and Sasebo Bay. The station at Kariya, on the northern side of Awaji township, is able to detect submarines approaching the Kobe–Osaka urban–industrial complex. In the case of Sasebo Bay, magnetic measurement stations were established at Sakibe, on the south-eastern side of the entrance to Sasebo Bay, built in 1976, and at Tategami, on the western side of the Sasebo port area, built in 1986.[24]

By the 1980s, 'enormous' magnetic detection systems had been mounted across the broader Tsushima and Tsugaru Straits. According to revelations in a Japanese 'novel' about Japan's plans for repelling a North Korean invasion, written by Iku Aso, a well-known journalist who specialises in intelligence matters, and first published in March 1998, which caused great anguish among the Japanese security authorities, these MAD systems detect the magnetic anomaly caused by submarines passing above them; these sensors can detect slower and quieter submarines that might elude the acoustic arrays. In the mid-1990s, after the Soviet Union had collapsed, this system reportedly monitored Russian missile submarines transiting to and from Vladivostok and Petropavlovsk, on the Pacific Ocean side of the Kamchatka Peninsula.[25]

Japan's Planned Ocean Surveillance Satellite Program

It was reported in July 2013 that Japan plans to launch nine satellites in the next five years to 'monitor the movements of foreign ships intruding into Japanese territorial waters'. The constellation will provide complete 24-hour coverage of all of the world's oceans, using infra-red sensors as well as other instruments.[26]

Japan began developing technologies for satellite-borne ocean remote sensing capabilities in the 1980s. For example, the Marine Observation Satellite (MOS)-1, launched on 19 February 1987, carried a Multispectral Electronic Self-Scanning Radiometer (MESSR); a Visible and Thermal Infra-red Radiometer

---

24 「崎辺地区海上自衛隊　佐世保市崎辺町」, 長崎平和委員会 [MSDF Sakibe District, Nagasaki Peace Committee], at www7b.biglobe.ne.jp/~chi-tan/sakibesdf.html; 「立神地区自衛隊　佐世保市立神町」, 長崎平和委員会 [MSDF Tategami District, Nagasaki Peace Committee], at www7b.biglobe.ne.jp/~chi-tan/tategamisdf.html

25 Iku Aso, *Sensen Fukoku* (Kodansha, Tokyo, March 1988), Vol. 1, pp. 91–92. See also 'Japan's North Korea War Plan Revealed in a "Novel"', *Shukan Gendai*, 4 April 1988, at www.kimsoft.com/1997/jp-dprk.htm

26 'Japan to Launch Satellites to Monitor Oceans', *Space Daily*, 7 July 2013, at www.spacedaily.com/reports/Japan_to_launch_satellites_to_monitor_oceans_999.html

(VTIR), to measure sea surface temperature (SST); and a Microwave Scanning Radiometer (MSR), to measure atmospheric water vapour. It was placed in a near-polar circular orbit, with an inclination of 99.1°, and an altitude of 909 kilometres. The second satellite in this series, MOS-1B, was launched on 7 February 1990.[27] The MOS program was succeeded by the Advanced Earth Observing Satellite (ADEOS) program, with ADEOS-1 (also called *Modori*-1) launched on 17 August 1996 and ADEOS-2 on 14 December 2002.[28]

27   Jet Propulsion Laboratory, 'Mission and Spacecraft Library: MOS 1A, 1B', at space.jpl.nasa.gov/msl/ QuickLooks/mosQL.html; FAO, 'Environmental Satellites', at www.fao.org/docrep/003/t0355e/t0355e05.htm
28   'ADEOS II', Wikipedia, at en.wikipedia.org/wiki/ADEOS_II

8. US SOSUS Stations

The US Navy was interested in Japanese locations for its SOSUS (sound surveillance system) stations from the beginning of its SOSUS program, initially called Project *Caesar*, which involved running cables out on continental shelves and connecting them to hydrophones suspended above the sea bottom at optimum signal depths. An 'experimental station' was established at the north-western tip of Hokkaido in 1957, with the cable extending into the Soya (La Perouse) Strait. It monitored all the submarine traffic going in and out of Vladivostok and Nakhodka in the Sea of Japan.[1] What was heard, however, 'didn't make sense because the collection of ship and submarine signatures was in its infancy at that time. It was a jumble of sounds'.[2] The jumble of sounds 'was largely undecipherable by existing signal processing'.[3]

Undersea surveillance systems and associated shore-based data collection stations code-named *Barrier* and *Bronco* were installed in Japan in the 1960s. These were reportedly similar to the *Caesar* system installed around the coasts of the United States but were 'located in coastal waters of friendly nations'. Acoustic data collected at these sites was transmitted by US defence communications satellites to US Navy processing and analysis centres in the United States.[4] According to a former US Navy intelligence officer:

> In the mid-1960s we offered to extend the CAESAR system to friendly countries – those that would allow CAESAR terminals to be installed as part of the Navy's overall world network. In Great Britain and Japan, systems were installed in the shallow coastal areas which had proven over the years to be the favorite exit points for Soviet submarines proceeding to the high seas. In 1967 there was congressional debate about extending CAESAR overseas, but testimony allayed Congressional fears that control of the system would slip beyond the Navy's reach.[5]

---

1 Jim Bussert, 'Computers Add New Effectiveness to SOSUS/CAESAR', *Defense Electronics*, October 1979, pp. 59–64; Larry Booda, 'Overview of ASW Systems and Their Capabilities', 13 March 1979, transcript.
2 Larry Booda, 'ASW: A Holding Action? Technical and Political Decisions Intermingle', *Sea Technology*, November 1978, p. 12.
3 Jim Bussert, 'Is SOSUS an Underwater Maginot Line?', *Military Electronics/Countermeasures*, July 1982, p. 43.
4 'Sonar – Sub-surface: Caesar', *DMS Market Intelligence Report* (DMS Inc, Greenwich, Connecticut, 1981); *Defense Electronics*, June 1983, p. 80.
5 Thomas S. Burns, *The Secret War for the Ocean Depths: Soviet-American Rivalry for Mastery of the High Seas* (Rawson Associates, New York, 1978), pp. 157–58.

The arrangements for assuring United States control evidently included stationing of US Navy personnel at the shore stations as well as the provision of satellite communications (Satcom) systems for the transmission of the acoustic data back to the United States.

There have been numerous reports about the locations of the US SOSUS stations in Japan. For example, a report prepared for the Committee on International Relations of the US House of Representatives in 1978 referred to a SOSUS array 'between Japan and Korea'.[6] An article on US and Allied SOSUS systems in 1980 identified three stations, at Wakkanai (designated JAP-4), Tsushima (JAP-108) and the Ryukyu Islands (RYU-80);[7] by this time the United States no longer had any SOSUS system in the Soya Strait, but relied on the Japanese station at Wakkanai to provide relevant information about the passage of Soviet submarines in that area. A map published in *Scientific American* in February 1981 also showed SOSUS shore facilities in the Tsushima Straits and the Okinawa area.[8] The existence of old cables at Horonai Point in north-west Honshu, which during the Cold War led out to SOSUS arrays in the Sea of Japan, has been widely described by scuba divers.[9] A study of US technical intelligence systems published in 1986 claimed that SOSUS hydrophone arrays stretched 'from southern Japan to the Philippines, covering the approaches to China and Indochina'.[10] The presence of SOSUS arrays sited off Okinawa was also reported in 1990.[11]

After the collapse of the Soviet Union and the decline of the submarine threat to the United States in the early 1990s, the US Navy allowed its SOSUS systems in the north-west Pacific to atrophy, although some arrays were retained in working order so as to support civilian scientific research (such as tracking whales and monitoring undersea volcanic activity). According to a navy directive issued in August 1994, all 'fixed arrays' in the Pacific were supposed to be placed on 'hot standby'; personnel would 'not be routinely assigned to monitor fixed array

---

6   Foreign Affairs and National Defense Division, Congressional Research Service, *Evaluation of Fiscal Year 1979 Arms Control Impact Statements: Toward More Informed Congressional Participation in National Security Policymaking* (US Government Printing Office, Washington, DC, 3 January 1978), p. 110.
7   'Militarisering av Haven: USA's Vapen Utvekling Rubbar Grunden for "Terrorbalansen"', *Kommentar*, October 1980, p. 22.
8   Joel S. Wit, 'Advances in Antisubmarine Warfare', *Scientific American* (Vol. 244, No. 2), February 1981, pp. 36–37.
9   Ronald F. Stark, 'Scuba Diving Sites: Popular Locations in the Aomori Prefecture', at divinewindadventures. com/Dive-Sites.htm; 'Sound Surveillance System (SOSUS)', Discovery of Sound in the Sea (DOSITS), at www. dosits.org/gallery/tech/pt/sosus1.htm.
10   William E. Burrows, *Deep Black: Space Espionage and National Security* (Random House, New York, 1986), p. 179.
11   Jane Dibblin, *Day of Two Suns: U.S. Nuclear Testing and the Pacific Islanders* (New Amsterdam Books, New York, 1990), p.195.

data' unless that data was required for operational purposes, but in practice the probability of being able to reconstitute them to full operational status was 'extremely low'.[12]

A decade later, however, in the early 2000s, facing an increasing Chinese submarine force and more aggressive Chinese submarine activities, the US Navy decided that it needed a new, more modern chain of fixed arrays designed primarily to monitor the movement of Chinese submarines between the East China Sea and South China Sea on the one hand, and the Pacific Ocean on the other hand. Described by an officer of the Taiwanese Military Intelligence Bureau in 2005 as the US Navy's 'Fish Hook Undersea Defense Line', it would stretch from Japan southwards to South-East Asia, with key nodes at Okinawa and Guam, another Cold War SOSUS site, and would utilise Allied undersea surveillance systems (most importantly, those of Japan and Taiwan) for key sections. Beginning from near Kagoshima in the south-west part of Kyushu, it would run down the Osumi archipelago to Okinawa, then to Miyako-jima and Yonaguni in the southern part of the Ryukyu Islands, past Taiwan to the Balabac Islands in the Philippines, to Lomkok in the eastern part of the Indonesian archipelago, across the Sunda Strait between Java and Sumatra, and from northern Sumatra to the Andaman Islands. Three major gaps, between Yonaguni and Suao in north-east Taiwan (120 kilometres), between Kaohsiung in south-western Taiwan and the Dongsha (Pratas) Islands (450 kilometres) where the East China Sea meets the South China Sea, and across the Bashi Channel (220 kilometres) between Hengchun at Taiwan's southernmost tip and Luzon Island in the Philippines, were identified around Taiwan (see Map 4).[13]

It seems that the US Navy installed a new SOSUS system, stretching from Sasebo down to Okinawa, in 2006, when the US cable-laying ship USNS *Zeus* operated together with oceanographic survey vessels and nuclear submarines in this area.[14] In July 2013, Beijing media reported that the United States and Japan had recently jointly established 'very large underwater monitoring systems' at the northern and southern ends of Taiwan. One of these stretched from Yonaguni to the Senkaku Islands (about 150 kilometres), while the other covered the Bashi Channel down to the Philippines. In addition, large numbers of hydrophones had been installed 'in Chinese waters' close to China's submarine bases.[15]

---

12 Dawn M. Maskell, 'The Navy's Best-Kept Secret: Is IUSS Becoming a Lost Art?', (Master's thesis, Marine Corps Command and Staff College, Quantico, Virginia, April 2001), at www.dtic.mil/cgi-bin/GetTRDoc?AD=ADA401150

13 Liao Wen-chung, 'U.S. Navy's Fish Hook Defense Line Submarine Monitoring Network in the West Pacific', *Defence International*, August 2005, at www.diic.com.tw/mag/mag252/252-74.htm

14 「ケーブル敷設艦・ 測量艦の佐世保入港増加の意味は？」['What is the Significance of an Increased Number of Sasebo Port Visits by Cable-laying Ships?'], Rimpeace, 1 September 2006, at www.rimpeace.or.jp/jrp/sasebo/sasebobase/0608ssbzeusags.html

15 'U.S. and Japan Work Together', *Beijing Daily*, 10 July 2013, at dailynews.sina.com/bg/chn/chnmilitary/sinacn/20130710/00164728365.html

Map 4. The US 'Fish Hook' Undersea Defense Line

Source: ANU CAP CartoGIS

9. JMSDF ELINT/Undersea Surveillance Stations

The Japanese Maritime Self-Defense Force (JMSDF) has at least 14 listening stations serving as shore terminals for the underwater hydrophone arrays, but which are typically also equipped with marine surveillance radars sites and electronic intelligence (ELINT) collection systems, and sometimes also with optical observation equipment. A report released by the Council on Security and Defense Capabilities in June 2004 identified 12 'coastal surveillance and intelligence collection' stations (including those at Rebun Island, Wakkanai and Shibetsu in northern Hokkaido identified with Japanese Ground Self-Defense Force (JGSDF) units).[1] The report did not, however, include the two ocean observation stations maintained by the Oceanographic Command, which have both been widely reported in other Japanese sources as having sound surveillance systems (SOSUS). Nor did it include Hachinohe, which was reportedly equipped with an LQO-3 system around 1970, but which may no longer be operational. Some of the Coastal Defense Stations established for harbour defence in the 1950s have been closed, such as one that was built at Awaji, in Osaka Bay, in 1957 but was closed in 1987, and another at Kogozaki, at the entrance to Sasebo Bay, which was opened in March 1959 and closed in June 1990.

The 14 identified operational stations are located at Noshyappu, at Wakkanai, at the tip of the cape that defines the southern side of the Soya Strait; Rebun Island, in the western approaches to the Soya Strait; Shibetsu, covering the eastern approaches to the Sea of Okhotsk and northern Hokkaido; Matsumae and Shirakami Saki, on the south-western point of Hokkaido, protruding into the Tsugaru Strait; Tappi Zaki, on the Tsugaru Peninsula in north-west Honshu, directly across the Tsugaru Strait from Shirakami Saki; Higashidori, on the Shimokita Peninsula; Kannon Zaki, at the entrance to Tokyo Wan (Bay); Kii, in Wakayama Prefecture, at the entrance from the Pacific Ocean to the Kii Strait and Osaka Bay; Mutsure-jima, at the western entrance to the Kanmon Strait and the Inland Sea; two stations on Tsushima Island (one on each of the North and South islands); Wakamiya, at the northern end of Iki Island, between Tsushima Island and Kyushu; and at the Ocean Observation Facility at White Beach on Okinawa (see Map 1 and Table 1).

---

1 「警戒監視情報の収集態勢（１）：陸上及び海上自衛隊」, アジア太平洋地域の安全保障環境と地域的な安全保障のための取組, 第５回「安全保障と防衛力に関する懇談会」資料, 平成１６年６月２９日 ['Maritime Surveillance and Intelligence Collection (1) JGSDF and JMSDF'], at www.kantei.go.jp/jp/singi/ampobouei/dai5/5siryou.pdf

Table 1. JMSDF ELINT/undersea surveillance sites

Site	Comments
1. Rebun Island, Hokkaido	JGSDF 301st Coastal Surveillance Unit.
2. Noshyappu, Wakkanai, Hokkaido	A single LQO-3 system installed around 1971. Replaced by an LQO-3A system in the early 1980s. JGSDF 301st Coastal Surveillance Unit. 301st Unit maintained a 36-element CDAA from 1988 to 2009. Replaced by a 7-element CDAA in 2009. Also 301st Unit at Maruyama, established in 1981.
3. Shibetsu, Hokkaido	JGSDF 302nd Coastal Surveillance Unit. Maintained a 36-element CDAA at Higashi Nemuro from 1991 to 2010. Replaced by a 7-element CDAA at JASDF SIGINT site at Nemuro in 2010. Associated unit at Rausu.
4. Matsumae, Hokkaido	New HQ building opened in 1968. New cable installed in 1971. Expanded and upgraded in 1990–91. US Navy team in the 1980s and 1990s.
5. Matsumae/Shirakami, Hokkaido	LQO-3 system installed in 1968. Replaced by an LQO-3A system in the early 1980s. Replaced by an LQO-4 system c. 1984.
6. Tappi Zaki, Aomori Prefecture, Honshu	LQO-3 system installed in 1968. Replaced by LQO-3A system in 1981–82. Replaced by an LQO-4 system around 1984.
7. Shimokita Peninsula, Higashidori, Aomori Prefecture	Shimokita-hanto Ocean Observation Station, Higashidori. Maintained by the JMSDF's Oceanographic Command.
8. Hachinohe, Aomori Prefecture	A single LQO-3 array reportedly installed in the 1970s.
9. Kannon Zaki, Tokyo Bay	
10. Kii, Hino-misaki, Wakayama Prefecture	Kii Guard Station became operational in December 1975. Probably initially equipped with an LQO-3 system, later replaced by an LQO-3A system.
11. Kami-tsushima, Tsushima Islands	LQO-3 system installed in 1968. Replaced by an LQO-3A system in the early 1980s. Replaced by an LQO-4 system around 1984.
12. Shimo-tsushima, Tsushima Islands	LQO-3 system installed in 1971–72. Replaced by an LQO-3A system in the early 1980s. Replaced by an LQO-4 system around 1984.

13. Mutsure-jima, Shimonoseki, Yamaguchi	Opened on 1 December 1957. Operated remotely from Shimonseki Guard Station. Surveillance radar installed in 2010.
14. Wakamiya, Iki Island	LQO-3 system installed in 1968. Replaced by an LQO-3A system in the early 1980s. Replaced by an LQO-4 system around 1984.
15. Kogozaki, Sasebo, Kyushu	Kogozaki Coastal Defense Station, Sasebo. US Navy anti-submarine net, 1945–59. US Navy — JMSDF Coastal Defense Station, March 1959 to May 1969. Returned to Japan in May 1969. Closed in June 1990, but buildings still maintained until the early 2000s. A Zeni Lite oceanographic navigation system installed in 1993.
16. White Beach, Katsuren, Okinawa	White Beach Ocean Observation Station, Katsuren. Maintained by the JMSDF's Oceanographic Command.
17. Yonaguni	JGSDF Coastal Surveillance Station under construction, to be operational in 2015. A hydrophone array reportedly installed around 2010.

In addition, it is likely that by the early 1980s, when the Japanese Government accepted the responsibility of defence of the sea lanes out to 1,000 nautical miles, the JMSDF had installed acoustic listening stations at various islands along the Honshu Ridge, running south from Tokyo Bay to the Marianas. The case for these stations was publicly articulated in 1971 in a detailed account of Japan's maritime defence requirements by Commander Hideo Sekino, a former JMSDF officer. He argued, after dismissing the likelihood of a Soviet conventional invasion of Hokkaido, that Japan's key strategic priority was defending its sea lanes against attacks by Soviet submarines and aircraft, that the JMSDF could control the Soya, Tsugaru, Shimonoseki and Tsushima Straits, thus inhibiting passage of the Soviet Pacific Fleet between the Sea of Japan and the Pacific Ocean, but that defence of the south-eastern approaches required extension of the underwater barrier by the establishment of listening stations at such places as the Izu Islands, just south of Tokyo Bay; the Ogasawaras (Bonin Islands); and Iwo Jima. Sekino estimated that a series of passive hydrophone and very low frequency (VLF) active sonar arrays dispersed at intervals along this island chain would ensure a 'high chance that targets would be detected during their passage from 100, or even 200 miles away', enabling 'patrol planes and helicopters based on some of these islands … to reach the points of detection within one hour'.[2]

Data collected by the undersea systems is relayed automatically by the shore stations to the Anti-submarine Warfare Center at the JMSDF's HQ at Yokosuka where it is 'bulk processed'. As of the late 1990s, the processed and correlated information was sent weekly to the Japan Defense Agency (JDA) HQ and the JMSDF's Maritime Staff Office. Data collected by the systems at Matsumae and Tsushima Island was reportedly also transmitted directly to the United States.[3] Data collected at the Shimokita-hanto and White Beach stations is probably also sent directly to the United States.

Wakkanai, Maruyama and Rebun Island

Wakkanai is located at the north-westernmost tip of Hokkaido, just 43 kilometres across the Soya (or La Perouse) Strait from Russia's Sakhalin Island. An observation station established in 1904 for monitoring Russian naval movements is a tourist attraction at Cape Soya, the northernmost point of Japan, 27 kilometres east of Wakkanai.

The US Navy at different times in the 1950s and 1960s conducted both undersea acoustic and ELINT activities at Wakkanai. The 'experimental' *Caesar* SOSUS station was established in 1957. According to a US Air Force officer who worked at the large US signals intelligence (SIGINT) station at Wakkanai in 1963–65, the US Navy in that period also maintained an ELINT unit there, code-named Operation *Cointreau*, which monitored the electronic emissions of Soviet submarines passing through the Soya Strait (which it called the 'Hokkaido Gate') and which was able to identify Soviet submarines 'by class, name and number'.[4]

The JMSDF laid a single LQO-3 hydrophone array from Noshyappu into the Soya Strait around 1970.[5] According to Japanese peace activists who researched some of the JMSDF's SOSUS sites, it was upgraded with an LQO-3A system in the early 1980s. The JMSDF is a tenant unit at the large Wakkanai SIGINT station, taken over by Japan from the United States in 1975.

---

2 Hideo Sekino, 'Japan and Her Maritime Defense', pp. 105, 120. See also James E. Auer, *Postwar Rearmament*, pp. 139–42; Euan Graham, *Japan's Sea Lane Security*, pp. 104–07.
3 Iku Aso, *Sensen Fukoku*, p. 92.
4 Bill Person, *Critic Makers: The Ironworks Incident* (Imprint Books, 2004), pp. 64, 200, 204.
5 Friedman, *Naval Institute Guide*, p. 21; Jeffrey T. Richelson, *Foreign Intelligence Organizations*, p. 261.

The primary responsibility for surveillance of the Soya Strait resides with the JGSDF's 301st Coastal Surveillance Unit, another tenant unit at the Wakkanai SIGINT station, where it had 40 personnel in 1988. In addition to ELINT capabilities, it maintains a 7-element circularly disposed antenna array (CDAA), constructed in 2009–10, for HF interception and HF DF operations (see Plate 1). (This replaced a 36-element system, with two concentric 18-element circles, which had been installed in 1987–88.) The 301st Communications Company provides the communication services for the 301st Coastal Surveillance Unit.

The JGSDF's 301st Coastal Surveillance Unit also maintains a detachment at Maruyama ('round mountain'), a 170-metre high rounded hill situated about 3 kilometres south of Cape Soya, which was established on 1 November 1981. It reportedly had 80 personnel in 1988. The operations building is a three-tiered concrete structure, with an 8-metre diameter radome atop the second tier and two 4-metre diameter radomes on the roof of the top tier. There are about 10 horizontal and vertical VHF/UHF log-periodic arrays (LPA) around the building, as well as a mast with 7-element UHF and VHF Doppler direction-finding (DF) arrays, and a microwave dish pointing south-west to Wakkanai (see Plate 2).

The 301st Coastal Surveillance Unit is the main unit at the SIGINT station on Rebun Island. Its existence was noted in a Japanese magazine in May 1987;[6] and it was described in reports by Japanese peace groups in the early 1990s.[7] It was established in 1979, and consists of a two-storey operations building; a 5-metre diameter radome near the north-western corner of the roof of the operations building; a three-storey building on the eastern side of the hill below the operations complex; a mast with four VHF LPAs on the northern side of the complex; a mast with 7-element UHF and VHF DF arrays identical to the one at Maruyama; and four tall masts holding HF wires (see Plate 3). Communications between Rebun Island and Wakkanai are provided by the 301st Communications Company.[8]

---

6   Tetsuo Kawamoto, 'Reorganization of Ground Self-Defense Force Divisions Seen', *Gunji Kenkyu*, May 1987, in Foreign Broadcast Information Service (FBIS), JPRS Report: East Asia, JPRS–JAR–87–005, 2 November 1987, pp. 11–12, at www.dtic.mil/dtic/tr/fulltext/u2/a346884.pdf

7   『北海度のC3I基地に見る新たな福強と変化』、松井愈　　（著者）、1993年日本平和会国際会議、C3I分科会・18th 全道基地闘争活動者会議（93・10 [Matsui Masaru, 'Looking at New Developments and Changes in Hokkaido C³I Bases, Japan Peace Committee International Conference, C3I Sub-committee; and 18th National Base Struggle Activists Conference (October 1993)', Hokkaido Peace Committee Study Document No. 26, 8–1994], p. 3 and map on back cover.

8   「警戒監視情報の収集態勢（１）：陸上及び海上自衛隊」，アジア太平洋地域の安全保障環境と地域的な安全保障のための取組，第５回「安全保障と防衛力に関する懇談会」資料，平成１６年６月２９日，['Maritime Surveillance and Intelligence Collection (1) JGSDF and JMSDF'], 29 June 2004, at www.kantei.go.jp/jp/singi/ampobouei/dai5/5siryou.pdf; 「礼文分屯地 」['Rebun Island Base'], Wikipedia – Japanese, at ja.wikipedia.org/wiki/%E7%A4%BC%E6%96%87%E5%88%86%E5%B1%AF%E5%9C%B0

Administrative and logistic support for the 301st Unit's facilities at Wakkanai, Maruyama and Rebun Island is provided by the JGSDF base at Nayoro, 160 kilometres south of Wakkanai. The 301st Communications Company has units at Nayoro and at Asahikawa for direct communications with the 301st Unit's stations at Rebun Island and Wakkanai.[9]

Shibetsu

Surveillance of the eastern entrance to the Sea of Okhotsk, through the Notsuke Sea, is the responsibility of the JGSDF's 302nd Coastal Surveillance Unit based at Shibetsu, in Nemuro district, in the north-east corner of Hokkaido. Shibetsu is about 23 kilometres across the Nemuro Strait from Kunashiri, at the southern end of the Kuril Islands chain. Shibetsu is one of the islands that were occupied by the Soviet Union in 1945 and which Japan claims as part of its Northern Territories. A hydrophone array is presumably fixed to the bottom of the strait and connected by cable to a convenient point on the shoreline near Shibetsu. The 302nd Unit at Shibetsu was identified by Japanese peace groups in the late 1980s.[10] Its HQ is situated in Shibetsu town, about five to six streets back from the shoreline. Organisationally, it is an 'operational unit' of the JGSDF's Kushiro Base, located about 100 kilometres south-west of Shibetsu. The 302nd Communications Company provides communications services for the unit.[11]

The 302nd Unit has three monitoring facilities located near Shibetsu. The main operations base is located at Kawakita, on a mountain ridge 19 kilometres west of Shibetsu.[12] There are five radomes covering interception systems, comprised of one with a diameter of about 11 metres situated on the ground at the front (facing the Nemuro Strait to the east), a green one mounted above the first one, with a diameter of about 6 metres, and three cylindrical thimbles with diameters

9   「名寄駐屯地」['JSDF Nayoro Camp'], Wikipedia – Japanese, at ja.wikipedia.org/wiki/%E5%90%8D %E5%AF%84%E9%A7%90%E5%B1%AF%E5%9C%B0; 「 旭川飛行場」['JGSDF Asahikawa Base'], Wikipedia – Japanese, at ja.wikipedia.org/wiki/%E6%97%AD%E5%B7%9D%E9%A3%9B%E8%A1%8 C%E5%A0%B4

10   『北海度のC3I基地に見る新たな福強と変化』、松井愈　　（著者）、1993年日本平和会国際会議、C3I分科会・18th 全道基地闘争活動者会議（93・10 [Matsui Masaru, 'Looking at New Developments and Changes in Hokkaido C³I Bases, Japan Peace Committee International Conference, C3I Sub-committee; and 18th National Base Struggle Activists Conference (October 1993)', Hokkaido Peace Committee Study Document No. 26, 8–1994], p. 3 and map on back cover.

11   国土地理院 [National Geographical Survey Institute], at watchizu.gsi.go.jp/watchizu.aspx?id=6545315 0&slidex=0&slidey=800; 標津分屯地」['Shibetsu Base'], Wikipedia – Japanese, at ja.wikipedia.org/wiki/% E6%A8%99%E6%B4%A5%E5%88%86%E5%B1%AF%E5%9C%B0

12   「 北方最前線！！　謎のレーダーサイト！？」、千島の桜 – Nakashibetsu Hokkaido ['Northern Frontline, Sakura of Chishima – Nakashibestu Hokkaido], 3 October 2009, at blogs.yahoo.co.jp/panzer_ tiger222/archive/2009/10/3

of about 5 metres located on top of a one-storey square room. There is also a steel tower with two microwave dishes pointing towards the JGSDF base in Shibetsu, and two other towers holding VHF antenna systems (see Plate 4).

The 302nd Coastal Surveillance Unit maintains another 'operational unit' at Rausu, on the eastern side of the Shiretoko Peninsula, about 25 kilometres from Kunashiri, and about 55 kilometres by road from Shibetsu. The Rausu facility comprises a three-storey building, about 10 metres high, with a 6-metre diameter radome on the roof, connected by an enclosed passageway to a two-storey administration and operations building. Behind these buildings is a tower with two microwave dishes on the side and 7-element UHF and VHF Doppler DF systems on the top identical to those at Maruyama and Rebun Island. About 20 metres away is another steel tower with three vertical VHF and four HF whip antennas (see Plate 5).

In 1993, the Shibetsu unit established facilities at the JASDF's SIGINT station at Nemuro, about 75 kilometres by road from Shibetsu. These are located north-west of the main JASDF complex, and consist of a two-storey operations building, a 12-metre diameter radome on top of the operations building, and four tall steel towers. The first two towers were built in 1993. One of these, on the north-west side of the operations building, has a small platform on top holding a VHF pole as well as both horizontal and vertical VHF LPAs (see Plate 6). The second tower, on the south-east side, holds a VHF/UHF DF system, with separate 5-element VHF and 5-element UHF arrays.[13]

The third and fourth towers were built between November 2007 and March 2010. One of these is on the south-west side of the compound, and holds a 5-element VHF and 5-element UHF DF system; it is similar but not identical to the VHF/UHF DF system on the second tower. The fourth tower is located on the eastern side of the JGSDF's compound and holds additional VHF LPA systems.

The 302nd Coastal Surveillance Unit also maintains a 7-element CDAA at the JASDF's Nemuro SIGINT station, built in 2010 (see Plate 7). (It has replaced a 36-element CDAA, similar to those previously located at Wakkanai and Kobunato, which was situated in Higashi Nemuro, on the Pacific coast, and which was constructed in 1991–92.[14] It was dismantled in September 2011.)

In addition, the JMSDF maintains a facility on the hook-shaped Notsuke Peninsula, at its closest point to Kunashiri (about 16 kilometres across the

13　『北海度のC3I基地に見る新たな福強と変化』、松井愈　（著者）、1993年日本平和会国際会議、C3I分科会・18th 全道基地闘争活動者会議（93・10 [Matsui Masaru, 'Looking at New Developments and Changes in Hokkaido C³I Bases, Japan Peace Committee International Conference, C3I Sub-committee; and 18th National Base Struggle Activists Conference (October 1993)', Hokkaido Peace Committee Study Document No. 26, 8–1994], pp. 10–11.
14　ibid., p. 12.

Nemuro Strait) and about 15 kilometres south-east of Shibetsu. It consists of a two-storey building situated on the seashore, with living quarters for about four staff on the ground floor and the observation rooms, equipped with large, high-magnification binoculars and camera, comprising the upper floor (see Plate 8). The hydrophone array across the Nemuro Strait is evidently connected to this building.

Matsumae and Shirakami

The JMSDF maintains two undersea surveillance shore stations near Hakodate, officially called Matsumae Coastal Defense Station and Shirakami Detachment of Matsumae Coastal Defense Station. The Matsumae Coastal Defense Station was established in 1968 (it celebrated its 35th anniversary on 1 May 2003).[15] Cape Shirakami is located about 7 kilometres south-east of Matsumae, and is the closest point in Hokkaido across the Tsugaru Strait to Honshu. Both places have long been used for surveillance of the entrance to the Strait. For example, a schematic map of Cape Shirakami that was drafted during the Second World War, when it was also a major artillery emplacement, shows two observation stations and an 'underwater listening station'.[16] Today, public entry to both sites is prohibited. A visitor seeking out the ruins of the Shirakami Artillery Station inside the prohibited area was told: 'Entry is forbidden because this is a most important national defence facility'.[17] It was reported in February 1985 that 'US civilians [worked] at the Shiragami guard post'.[18]

Five LQO-3 arrays were installed in the Tsugaru Strait in the late 1960s and early 1970s.[19] The first two, installed in 1967–68, were presumably located at Tappi Zaki and Shirakami, the narrowest part of the Strait. 'All the buildings' at both Shirakami and Tappi Zaki were completely renovated in the 1980s, and 'the underwater microphones were also changed from the LQO-3s to new model LQO-4s'.[20] Cables to the hydrophone arrays enter the sea at the Shintakano Bridge, about 3 kilometres west of the Shirakami station. The ELINT systems at Shirakami include antennas housed in a large hemispherical radome and in

---

15 「北海道地方」、『自衛隊イベント情報 [2003年版] 』 ['Hokkaido: Information on JSDF Events 2003'], at www003.upp.so-net.ne.jp/rightwing/event/2003/hokkaido2003.html
16 「 白神岬砲台」 ['Shirakami-misaki Battery'], at www006.upp.so-net.ne.jp/fortress/tsugaru/shirakami.htm
17 ibid.
18 'White Paper: Nuclear War and the Self-Defense Forces', at www.dtic.mil/cgi-bin/GetTRDoc?Location=U2&doc=GetTRDoc.pdf&AD=ADA349828
19 Naoaki Usui, 'Japan Plans to Bolster Already Formidable ASW Ability', p. 14.
20 'White Paper: Nuclear War and the Self-Defense Forces', at www.dtic.mil/cgi-bin/GetTRDoc?Location=U2&doc=GetTRDoc.pdf&AD=ADA349828

a cylindrical radome, a discone omnidirectional UHF DF system, and two VHF LPAs, one pointing to the south-west and the other to the south-east (see Plate 9).

The main Matsumae site is better placed for the landing point of a longer cable reaching out to the middle of the Sea of Japan and using the US-supplied deep-water, long-range hydrophone array and long cable installed in 1972. It is located above a 20-metre cliff, on the north-western side of the JMSDF's harbour (see Plate 10). According to accounts by local fishermen, the *Tsugaru* cable-laying ship connected a long cable to the Matsumae station in 1972. They said that for 'dozens of years', two cables could be seen coming out of the cliff. During the 1970s, the area at the base of the cliff was covered by large concrete blocks to prevent storm damage, but the presence of four cables was reported by Hokkaido peace groups in the early 1980s. These reports also described a three-storey 'observation/surveillance' building, with a 'secret underground room', and recorded that at least 200 JMSDF personnel were stationed at the Matsumae base.[21]

The Matsumae station was substantially expanded in 1991–92. A new facility, with an underground computer building, was built on the western side of the existing HQ. Reports by Hokkaido peace groups in the early 1990s noted that the historical purpose of the station was to monitor ships passing through the Tsugaru Strait, but that a 1,000-kilometre-long cable had also been installed at the station, which extended the coverage across the Sea of Japan, enabling traffic leaving Vladivostok Bay and entering from the Sea of Okhotsk to be monitored. They also noted that a group of Russian linguists worked at the station, and that the station listened to the sounds of the propellers on Soviet submarines. They said that a small US unit had been stationed at the base for many years, usually involving six to eight personnel, mainly women, and that a new team was working in the building constructed in 1992.[22]

Photographs of the operations area in 1992 show a microwave tower with two dishes next to the operations building, a stand with three hemispherical radomes, a cylindrical radome on the roof of a building, and a tower with two hemispherical radomes and one cylindrical radome. Three radars and four other antennas were situated on the hill above the station.[23] Recent high-resolution Google Earth imagery shows no apparent changes to this infrastructure.

---

21 'Sea-bottom Cable-laying Ship Operating Offshore', *Asahi Shimbun*, 17 June 1984.
22 『北海度のC3I基地に見る新たな福強と変化』、松井愈　（著者）、1993年日本平和会国際会議、C3I分科会・18th 全道基地闘争活動者会議（93・10 [Matsui Masaru, 'Looking at New Developments and Changes in Hokkaido C³I Bases, Japan Peace Committee International Conference, C3I Sub-committee; and 18th National Base Struggle Activists Conference (October 1993)', Hokkaido Peace Committee Study Document No. 26, 8–1994], pp. 4–5.
23 ibid., pp. 2, 5.

Tappi Zaki

Tappi Zaki, in Aomori prefecture, is located at the north-westernmost point of Honshu. It is a windswept outcropping of land, noted for its severe gales, with its cliffs battered by the seas. On a clear day, it is possible to see Shirakami across the Tsugaru Strait. The two sides are connected by the 35-kilometre under-seabed Seikan Tunnel. A naval observation post was built at Tappi Zaki in July 1901, and 'coastal hydrophone' arrays were laid in the Tsugaru Strait off Tappi Zaki in the 1930s. A first-generation hydrophone system was installed off Tappi Zaki in the 1950s; it was replaced by an LQO-3 system in 1968, which was in turn replaced by an LQO-3A system in 1981–82. There were 35 personnel at the station in the late 1980s.

Photographs of the Tappi Zaki facility show a hemispherical radome with a diameter of about 1 metre, containing an ELINT/ electronic support measures (ESM) antenna, two VHF radio masts, meteorological antennas and, until around 2007, an increasing number of microwave dishes. The ELINT/ESM radome was installed with construction of the LQO-3A system in early 1982. In the case of the microwave dishes, photographs show one in March 1981, before the removal of the LQO-3 system, pointing eastwards towards Ominato/Shimokita Peninsula; three in June 1982, two pointing eastwards and one pointing north-west towards Matsumae/Cape Shirakami; and three in November 1990, one pointing eastwards and two pointing north-west. There were four in 2000 and in 2002; the fourth was mounted on a separate short tower and pointed eastwards.[24] Sometime between August 2006 and November 2008, however, all of the dishes were removed, presumably because the microwave network was replaced by optical fibre cables for communication connections (see Plate 11).

During the Cold War, another set of cables connected to SOSUS arrays entered the sea at Horonai Point, a small man-made bay enclosed by natural rock on one side and cement tetrapods and boulders on the other, just over a kilometre south of Tappi Zaki; the cables run straight out until they vanish into the gravel bottom at the 20-metre level.[25] According to one report, three cables 'extend out into the Sea of Japan on a bearing of 330 degrees'. They are evidently no longer used and 'have fallen prey to anchors and corrosion'.[26]

---

24 See www.fitweb.or.jp/~red2000/tappizaki.jpg; 「ごらんあれが竜飛岬」 ['Look, there is Tappizaki'], 'Out Camping with my Dog', at www11.plala.or.jp/kei-home/nikki-13-tappi-1.htm
25 'Scuba Diving: Aomori', *Outdoor Japan*, at www.outdoorjapan.com/activities/scuba/scuba-diving-ag-aomori.html; Ronald F. Stark, 'A Diving Instructor's Journal: 2001 Adventures', 15 November 2001, at www.heronet.ne.jp/~rfstark/Log2001.htm; Ronald F. Stark, 'Divine Wind Adventures: Dive Report 20 June 2009', at www.divewindadventures.com/frame contents.htm; Stark, 'Scuba Diving Sites', at divinewindadventures.com/Dive-Sites.htm; 'Tappizaki Diving of the Tsugaru Peninsula', at www.japanguides.net/aomori/tappizaki-diving-of-the-tsugaru-peninsula.html
26 'Sound Surveillance System (SOSUS)', at www.dosits.org/gallery/tech/pt/sosus1.htm

A Chinese navy intelligence vessel, the *Yanbing* 723, a converted 4,420-ton icebreaker that collects SIGINT for its North Sea Fleet, conducted electronic surveillance operations in the Tsugaru Strait in May 2000. Equipped with an extensive variety of radar and other antenna systems, the spy ship had 'conducted surveillance operations in waters around Tsushima for seven days from May 14', before proceeding north and passing through the Tsugaru Strait three times from 23 to 26 May. It accorded particular attention to the Tappi Zaki 'guard station'.[27] The Japanese Foreign Minister complained about the incident to his Chinese counterpart at a meeting in July, but his plaint was dismissed.[28]

Shimokita-hanto Ocean Observation Station

The Shimokita-hanto Ocean Observation Station is located in the Odanosawa–Aranuma area in Higashidori, in Aomori Prefecture, facing the Pacific Ocean, just south of Shiriya-saki, the north-easternmost point of Honshu, and well-placed to monitor approaches to the eastern entrance to Tsugaru Strait. It was identified as the location of a SOSUS system by Japanese peace groups in several reports in the early 1990s.[29] It is described as a SOSUS site on the Japanese Wikipedia website.[30]

Organisationally, the station consists of a commander, a deputy commander, and seven departments: the Ocean Observation Department, which operates the SOSUS system; Analysis Department, which is responsible for analysis, organisation and storage of the data; Supply Department, which manages logistic and catering requirements; Internal Affairs Department, which is concerned with personnel, administration and maintenance matters; Development Department, responsible for maintenance and upgrading of the oceanographic equipment; Health Department, which provides medical services for the station's personnel; and the Communications Department, which operates and maintains the communications equipment.[31]

---

27 'Chinese Vessel Found to Have Conducted Operations Off Boso Peninsula, Gathering Radio Wave Information During Voyage Around the Japanese Archipelago, Says MSDF', *Sankei*, 10 June 2000, in American Embassy, Tokyo, 'Daily Summary of Japanese Press', 14 June 2000; NIDS, *East Asian Strategic Review 2001*, pp. 200–02.
28 'Reviewing ODA or China Policy?: Tokyo Only Expressed Fears', at chinaperspectives.revues.org/document358.html
29 『北海度のC3I基地に見る新たな福強と変化』、松井愈　　（著者）、1993年日本平和会国際会議、C3I分科会・18th 全道基地闘争活動者会議（93・10 [Matsui Masaru, 'Looking at New Developments and Changes in Hokkaido C³I Bases, Japan Peace Committee International Conference, C3I Sub-committee; and 18th National Base Struggle Activists Conference (October 1993)', Hokkaido Peace Committee Study Document No. 26, 8–1994], map on back cover.
30 「下北海洋観測所」['Shimokita Ocean Observation Station'], Wikipedia – Japanese, at ja.wikipedia.org/wiki/%E4%B8%8B%E5%8C%97%E6%B5%B7%E6%B4%8B%E8%A6%B3%E6%B8%AC%E6%89%80
31 ibid.

The Technical Research and Development Institute (TRDI) also has its Shimokita Test Center in the Naganuma–Aranuma area.[32] It is one of the TRDI's original test centres, dating back to the late 1950s.[33] It includes a proscribed offshore 'experimental' area, extending for about 12 kilometres along the coastline, adjacent to the ocean observation station.

The Maritime Safety Agency (MSA)/Japan Coast Guard (JCG) maintains a lighthouse and radio beacon for direction-finding purposes at Shiriya-saki, famous for its wild Kandachime horses. The lighthouse was bombed during the Second World War, killing the keeper and destroying the structure. The present complex is adorned with a variety of antennas, including a HF wire strung between two tall poles over the entrance to the lighthouse complex, a tall tower with two VHF whips on top, two VHF whips and a VHF yagi on the roof of the two-storey building next to the lighthouse, and a microwave dish on the side of the building. The radio beacon/Differential GPS (DGPS) facility is situated about 50 metres from the lighthouse complex, and consists of a small shack with a tall HF ground-plane antenna, a satellite communications antenna on the side of the building, and the DGPS system, which comprises four small orbs, about 100 centimetres in diameter, atop four masts in a square. The radio-beacon transmits a 75-watt continuous wave (CW) signal on a frequency of 9.037 megahertz, with a nominal range of 200 kilometres.

Hachinohe

The existence of a station at Hachinohe is uncertain. An LQO-3 array was reportedly installed near Hachinohe around 1971, for monitoring traffic through the eastern entrance to the Tsugaru Strait.[34] The location should have made it a prime candidate for installation of an LQO-4 array, the longer range system deployed in the late 1980s; the LQO-4 provided broader ocean surveillance for cueing the JMSDF's P-2J maritime patrol aircraft, for which Hachinohe was one of the main operational bases. Photographs of a JMSDF HF antenna farm at Hachinohe in the late 1980s, said to be for collecting ocean surveillance information, show some 17 tall poles, one located adjacent to a small hut in the centre of the array, an inner group of eight and an outer group of another eight. Hachinohe was not, however, included in the map produced by the Council on Security and Defense Capabilities in June 2004; it was perhaps superseded by the facilities at the ocean observation station at Higashidori, only 90 kilometres to the north.

---

32 'Technical Research and Development Institute: Research Centers Addresses', at www.mod.go.jp/trdi/en/misc/address.html; 'TRDI: Shimokita Test Center', at www.mod.go.jp/trdi/en/research/simokita_test_en.html.
33 Auer, *Postwar Rearmament*, pp. 220–21.
34 Richelson, *Foreign Intelligence Organizations*, p. 261.

Kannon Zaki

Kannon Zaki is located on the Miura peninsula, at the south-western entrance to Tokyo Bay, just south of the Yokosuka JMSDF/US Navy base. The area has many remnants of military facilities from the Meiji, Taisho and early Showa eras. The site was used for a Japanese navy radar station during the Second World War.[35] It is just 6.5 kilometres from Kannon Zaki across the Uraga Channel to Futtsu Misaki, or 8 kilometres to Isone Misaki, in Chiba Prefecture.

There are four substantial facilities in the area, including the famous Kannon Zaki lighthouse, which is regularly visited by tourists; the JCG's Tokyo Bay Vessel Traffic Control Facility, on the northern side of the promontory; and two JMSDF facilities.

The Kannon Zaki Coastal Defense Station was originally established in the 1950s as the Yokosuka Guard Unit. On 2 December 1957, Japan and the United States signed an agreement for a loan for 'defence materials' for the Kannon Zaki station, as well as for a similar station at Kogozaki, near Sasebo. It was organised as the Kannon Zaki Coastal Defense Station of the Yokosuka Coastal Defense Group on 1 April 1960.[36]

The Kannon Zaki Coastal Defense Station is situated close to the shoreline on the southern side of the peninsula, access to which is blocked off, a few hundred metres from the lighthouse. It comprises a two-storey building and several smaller buildings, together with several HF antennas, including a large HF curtain array.

A complementary facility is situated on the crown of the hill behind the lighthouse; it is surrounded by a wire-netting fence, with the entrance and guard post on the western side. It has a marine surveillance radar and a hemispheric ESM radome, several tall HF antennas, and eight to ten other sensor and antenna systems.

It is likely that at least two hydrophone arrays are deployed in the area, with one strung across the Uraga Channel to detect submarines entering Tokyo Bay, and another situated to provide a proximate defence of the eastern approaches to the JMSDF/US Navy complex at Yokosuka.

The JCG's Tokyo Bay Traffic Advisory Service Center is responsible for ensuring that 'hundreds of vessels a day [from huge cargo ships over 10,000 tons to small fishing boats] can safely navigate in one of the world's busiest and most

---

35   *Operational History of Japanese Naval Communications, December 1941–August 1945* (Aegean Park Press, Laguna Hills, California, 1985), pp. 122–23.
36   'The History of Mine-sweeper Units', at www.dii.mod.go.jp/msdf/mf/rekishi/rekishi-1.htm

congested waterways'. Larger vessels are supposed to notify the centre of their anticipated entry into the bay by noon the previous day. Cameras, radars and even binoculars are used to identify and tag every vessel passing through the Uraga Strait.[37] There are two towers with six to eight microwave dishes adjacent to the main building. Data on vessel movements and identities is presumably routinely passed to the JMSDF's Coastal Defense Station for correlation purposes.

In addition, the National Defense Academy maintains a maritime training facility in Hashirimizu Port in Yokosuka, about 1.5 kilometres north-west of the Tokyo Bay Traffic Advisory Service Center, which includes at least two sets of 4-element Bruel & Kjaer (B&K) Type 8105 hydrophone arrays, noted for their 'excellent directional characteristics'.[38] These arrays have been used to determine 'biological transient noises' that complicate submarine detection in Tokyo Bay. For example, in August 2007, a single hydrophone was used to record sounds typical of those produced by 'snapping shrimp'. In August 2009, two sets of 4-element arrays were used to measure the sounds of 'snapping shrimp' and to estimate 'the positions of those noise sources'. In October 2009, 'a pair of tetrahedral arrays' was also used to estimate the 'source positions' of such noises.[39]

Kii

The Kii facility is located on Hino-misaki, in the Enjukaigan Prefectural Natural Park, at the most western edge of the Kii Peninsula in Wakayama Prefecture, in the south-east corner of Honshu (see Plates 12 and 13). Organisationally, it is part of the JMSDF's Hanshin base. A sign in front of the nearby lighthouse says that it was attacked by the United States on 30 July 1945 and rebuilt in 1951. The JMSDF station became operational in December 1975. Its duty is to monitor the Kii channel and to collect information concerning the security of the waterways, coastline and harbours in the area. It was commanded by Ensign Yamashita Hiroshi in 2006.[40]

---

37   Steven L. Herman, 'Auxiliarist Reporter/Translator Works to Enhance Relationship with Japan Coast Guard', at www.teamcoastguard.org/2005/May/A050521/japan.htm

38   Bruel & Kjaer, 'Product Data: Hydrophones – Types 8103, 8104, 8105 and 8106', at www.lthe.fr/LTHE/IMG/pdf/DocBruelKjaerHydro.pdf

39   Haruki Kada, Kazuyoshi Mori, Hanako Ogasawara, Toshiaki Nakamura, Takenobu Tsuchiya & Nobuyki Endoh, 'Preliminary Result of Biological Transient Noise Observation Using 2 Sets of 4-Element Hydrophone Array', *Proceedings of Symposium on Ultrasonic Electronics* (Vol. 30), 18–20 November 2009, pp. 165–66, at www.use-jp.org/USE2010/proceedings/USE09/pdf/1P6-7.pdf; Kazuyoshi Mori, Hanako Ogasawara and Toshiaki Nakamura, 'Observation Results for Biological Impulsive Noise at Hashirimizu Port in Tokyo Bay', *Memoirs of the National Defense Academy* (Vol. 51, No. 1), May 2011, pp. 1–12.

40   「紀伊警備所」、JMSDF阪神基地 ['Kii Guard Station', JMSDF Hanshin Base], at www.mod.go.jp/msdf/hanshin/about/kii/index.html

It initially complemented the Awaji Guard Station, about 75 kilometres further north, but on the western side of Osaka Bay, at the north-western corner of Awaji Island, and only 30 kilometres from the Kobe–Osaka urban–industrial complex, which was built in 1957. It overlooked Akashi Strait, linking the Inland Sea with Osaka Bay, only 3.6 kilometres across, shallow on both sides, and having a depth only about 100 metres in its central channel. The Awaji station was closed in July 1987. The Kii station was also downgraded in 1987.[41]

An ESM radome is located on a hill, 201.5 metres above sea level, about 500 metres behind the JMSDF station; it is mounted on a 5-metre tower on top of a small cement building (see Plate 14). A microwave tower is situated near the lighthouse. Photographs taken in August 2006 show only one microwave dish, whereas previously there had been four, suggesting that optical fibre cables may have been installed for transmission of data traffic from the station.

In July 2000, the *Dongdiao* 232, a Yanqian-class marine survey ship used by the Chinese navy's South Sea Fleet for intelligence collection purposes, engaged in 'intelligence gathering activities' off the Kii Peninsula.[42]

The Hanshin base also employs a magnetic measurement station at Kariya, on the northern side of Awaji township.[43] It is able to detect submarines approaching the Kobe–Osaka urban–industrial complex.

Mutsure-jima

The small and sparsely inhabited island of Mutsure-jima is located near Shimonoseki in Yamaguchi Prefecture, at the entrance to the Kanmon Strait, separating Honshu and Kyushu, and the western entrance to the Inland Sea. The JMSDF's Mutsure-jima Coastal Defense Station is located near the northern end of the island, at the highest point on the island (106 metres). From Mutsure-jima east to the mainland is only 5 kilometres, while south-west to the north-east point of Kyushu is about the same distance.

The station was initially established as Shimonoseki Guard Station, part of the Shimonoseki Base Group of the Sasebo District Command, on 1 December 1957.[44] Google Earth images show two main buildings, a hemispherical ESM radome, a circular antenna array, and several other sensor and antenna systems (see

---

41   ibid.
42   NIDS, *East Asian Strategic Review 2001*, p. 202.
43   「仮屋磁気測定所, 阪神基地隊について」, ['Kariya Magnetic Measurement Station, Hanshin Base Group], JMSDF, at www.mod.go.jp/msdf/hanshin/about/kariya/index.html
44   「六連警備所」海上自衛隊 ['Mutsure Coastal Defense Station', MSDF], at www.dii.jda.go.jp/msdf/mf/rekishi/rekishi-1.htm; 「下関基地」 'Shimonoseki Base', Wikipedia – Japanese, at ja.wikipedia.org/wiki/%E4%B8%8B%E9%96%A2%E5%9F%BA%E5%9C%B0.

Plate 15). A rotating surveillance radar is located about 100 metres north of the station (see Plate 16). A visitor to the station on 4 August 2010 noted that it had been 'recently installed'.[45] Both the ELINT/ESM station and the radar are operated remotely from the Shimonoseki Guard Station. Three JMSDF officers were at the station on 7 October 2010; they were members of the Electronics Unit of the Maintenance and Supply Squadron of the Shimonoseki Guard Station, and were performing routine maintenance of the electronic equipment.

Tsushima Island

Tsushima Island, in the Korea Strait off south-western Japan, consists of two mountainous islands, Kamino-shima (the north island) and Shimono-shima (the south island), which are connected by a combination bridge and causeway. It is the closest Japanese territory to Korea, being only 50 kilometres from Pusan, the lights of which are visible on clear nights. It is about 70 kilometres from north-western Kyushu, across the Tsushima Strait and it has historically served as both a forward defence post against attacks from Russia, Korea and China against Japan's southern flank and a staging point for Japanese forays against Korea and China. In the 7th century, frontier guards called Sakimori were stationed and signal fires prepared on Tsushima Island and Iki Island in the Tsushima Strait as a defence against Chinese and Korean invaders.[46] In the 13th century, in the Kamakura period, the guards on Tsushima and Iki Islands fought desperately against Kublai Khan's Mongol forces in 1274 and 1281, contributing to the failure of the attempted invasions of Kyushu.[47] Tsushima and Iki, as well as Mutsure-jima, were the home bases of the Japanese Wokou pirates who raided the Korean and Chinese coastlines from the 13th to the 16th centuries.[48] The Battle of Tsushima in May 1905, when the Japanese Combined Fleet annihilated the Russian Fleet, described at the time by Julian Corbett as 'the most decisive and complete naval victory in history', took place just east of Tsushima Island and north of Iki Island, as the Russian Fleet was steaming in column through the Tsushima Strait.[49]

45　「六連島探検 ― 自衛隊元レーダー基地編」、 彦中三八ブログ ['Exploring Mitsurejima : Former SDF Radar Station', Hikochu 38 Blog], 4 August 2010, at blog.goo.ne.jp/hikochu38sotu/e/fe817565af03a92589fc4a77ddf1c6a6

46　Bruce Batten, 'The Founding of Dazaifu', 6 October 2004, at www.fukuokahistory.com/live/content/view/15/52/; Ono Yasumaru, 'Preface to the Chronicle "Kojiki"', at www.geocities.jp/general_sasaki/oono-yasu-eng.html

47　Richard Storry, *A History of Modern Japan* (Penguin, Harmondsworth, Middlesex, 1960), p. 40; Malcolm Kennedy, *A Short History of Japan* (Mentor, New York, 1964), pp. 59–60.

48　'Wokou', Wikipedia, at en.wikipedia.org/wiki/Wokou; 'Iki Island', Wikipedia, at wikipedia.org/wiki/Iki_Island

49　Julian S. Corbett & Edmond J.W. Slade, *Maritime Operations in the Russo–Japanese War* (Admiralty War Staff, London 1914, reprinted by Naval Institute Press, Annapolis, Maryland, 1994), Vol. 2, p. 333; David C. Evans & Mark R. Peattie, *Kaigun*, p. 124.

The JMSDF has three primary stations on Tsushima, comprising a large HQ base (at Mitsushima) and two shore stations for undersea surveillance systems (at Kami-tsushima and Shimo-tsushima), and several support facilities. Five LQO-3 hydrophone arrays were installed in the Tsushima Strait in 1968–72, including two in 1968 and one in 1972, connected to the two shore stations on Tsushima as well as a third station on Iki Island.[50] Seven LQO-4 systems were installed in the early 1980s, at which time a US Navy SOSUS system was 'also deployed'.[51]

The Tsushima Coastal Defense Group HQ is located at Takeshiki harbour in Mitsushima, on the north-eastern side of the south island. Takeshiki harbour was established as a torpedo boat base in 1886. After the Sino–Japanese war in 1894, it became a strategic port for forward defence against Russia. The Tsushima Defense Office of Sasebo Base was established at Mitsushima/Takeshiki in December 1954. It was renamed Tsushima Coastal Defense Detachment of Sasebo Base in March 1960. It became Tsushima Coastal Defense Group HQ in March 1970, at which time it assumed operational command of the three SOSUS shore stations at Kami-tsushima, Shimo-tsushima and Iki Island. The HQ has microwave links to two microwave relay stations, one located at Gongen-yama, near Iduhara, which was established in January 1966, and which provides a direct link with the Shimo-tsushima station at Iduhara, and the other at Shirotake, which was built in November 1966.[52]

The Kami-tsushima station is located in Kami-tsushima town, in Ooura district, at the north-western end of the north island. It has been described as 'a real creepy place that's sort of an island just at the top of Tsushima'.[53] It had previously been the site of the massive 'Toyo battery' and associated observatory, built in 1934 to command the Korea Strait.[54]

The JMSDF's Kami-tsushima station was established as an Observation Unit of the Sasebo Regional District HQ, with a surveillance radar, ELINT equipment and a first-generation hydrophone array, in 1960. It became the Kami-tsushima Guard Station of Sasebo Base in 1967 and a subsidiary station of the Tsushima Coastal Defense Group HQ in March 1970.[55] In the late 1960s, beginning on

---

50 Naoaki Usui, 'Japan Plans to Bolster Already Formidable ASW Ability', p. 14; 第０６７回国会、沖縄及び北方問題に関する特別委員会、第１号、昭和四十六年十二月二十八日 [67th Diet, Special Committee on Okinawa and the Northern Problem, 18 December 1971], at kokkai.ndl.go.jp/SENTAKU/sangii n/067/1650/06712281650001c.html

51 'White Paper: Nuclear War and the Self-Defense Forces', at www.dtic.mil/cgi-bin/GetTRDoc?Location= U2&doc=GetTRDoc.pdf&AD=ADA349828

52 「対馬防備隊」 ['Tsushima Defense Group Headquarters'], Wikipedia – Japanese, at ja.wikipedia.org/wiki/%E5%AF%BE%E9%A6%AC%E9%98%B2%E5%82%99%E9%9A%8A

53 'Crisscross Discussion' on 'Officer Being Investigated for Trips to China Found Hanged on MSDF Destroyer in Sasebo', 10 August 2006, at www.crisscross.com/jp/news/381183

54 「上対馬警備所」、長崎平和委員会 ['Kamitsushima Guard Station', Nagasaki Peace Committee], at www7b.biglobe.ne.jp/~chi-tan/kamitsushima.html

55 ibid.

9 August 1966, the station reported several instances of intrusions by Soviet warships into Japanese territorial waters, but the JMSDF lacked the requisite capability to effectively respond.[56]

The Kami-tsushima station occupies an area of nearly 33,000 square metres, on a hilltop about 120 metres above sea level. The operations building has two storeys, with a radar room and ELINT processing equipment on the first floor, and a 'monitoring room' with a 'sophisticated telescope' on the second floor. It is connected to a SOSUS-type array consisting of 'hundreds of ultra-low-frequency acoustic detection sensors' fixed to the seabed across the northern end of the Korea Strait. A heliport was built at the station in 1975.[57]

The station had at least 19 antenna systems, located on the roof of the operations building and atop adjoining structures, in October 2010. These consisted of a hemispherical ELINT/ESM radome, similar to those at nearly all the JMSDF's ELINT stations; a large cylindrical radome; two conical radomes (presumably containing omnidirectional ESM/DF systems monitoring radar emissions, with a DF accuracy of 5–10 degrees); a 4-element VHF DF system and a 4-element UHF DF system; a marine surveillance radar; six large crossed VHF LPAs, two pointing towards the west, two to the north-west, and two to the south-west; a small 'box'-type UHF antenna system; two HF/VHF poles; two small cylindrical systems; and a microwave dish for local communications (see Plate 17). In addition, there is an associated tower with another hemispherical ELINT/ESM radome and two microwave dishes at Kin, in the northeast part of the north island.

The Shimo-tsushima station is situated about 8 kilometres south of Iduhara, or about 20 kilometres south of Mitsushima, in Agami district, about midway along the eastern side of the south island. During the Second World War, the site housed a fortified artillery battery. The Shimo-tsushima Guard Station was established in March 1969. It was initially directly controlled by the Sasebo Regional District HQ, but in March 1970 it became subordinate to the Tsushima Coastal Defense Group HQ at Mitsushima. It has a branch office at Hisadamati in Iduhara-cho. It cooperates closely with the Iki Island Guard Station.[58]

The operations building of the Shimo-tsushima station is located on a hilltop about 2 kilometres from the living quarters. The Shimo-tsushima station was reportedly equipped with an LQO-3 hydrophone array in 1972.[59] Photographs taken by peace activists show at least seven antennas on the roof of the main

---

56 Auer, *Postwar Rearmament*, p. 167.
57 「上対馬警備所」、長崎平和委員会 ['Kamitsushima Guard Station', Nagasaki Peace Committee], at www7b.biglobe.ne.jp/~chi-tan/kamitsushima.html
58 「下対馬警備所」、長崎平和委員会 ['Shimotsushima Guard Station', Nagasaki Peace Committee], at www7b.biglobe.ne.jp/~chi-tan/shimotsushima.html
59 'Sea-bottom Cable-laying Ship Operating Offshore'.

building, including an ELINT/ESM radome. There are also several antennas on an adjoining tall tower, including three microwave dishes and an ESM system at the top (see Plates 18 and 19). Two of the microwave dishes are directed at the Gongen-yama relay station, while the third points towards relay stations at Ikarikuma-yama and Tsutsu-Ozaki-yama. A heliport was also built at the station in 1975.[60] An associated tower with a hemispherical ELINT/ESM radome and a microwave dish is located at Tsutsu, in the south-west part of the south island (see Plate 20).

The JGSDF also has two 'coastal monitoring training areas' on Tsushima Island, one located at Mitsushima and the other at Kami-tsushima.[61] The Mitsushima facility was established in 1956, with an area of 33,054 square metres; this was increased to 96,791.31 square metres in 1986, and to 260,709.54 square metres around 2002. The facility includes a training ground used for 'coastal monitoring field exercises', a 'coastal warning and surveillance capability', and a combat unit with a 'limited ability to protect the coastal region'.[62]

It was revealed in August 2006 that the capabilities and operations of the JMSDF's surveillance facilities on Tsushima may have been seriously compromised. A 45-year-old Petty Officer First Class, who had worked as a communications officer at the Kami-tsushima Guard Station from April 2004 to July 2006, was transferred to Sasebo, suspended from duty, and placed under investigation for suspected divulgence of secrets to Chinese intelligence agents. The officer had made eight trips to Shanghai between January 2005 and March 2006, where he was having an affair with a hostess at a karaoke club used by Chinese intelligence for 'honey trap' operations. A search of his private residence in April found 'large quantities of CDs containing pictures of military warships

---

60   「下対馬警備所」、長崎平和委員会 ['Shimotsushima Guard Station', Nagasaki Peace Committee], at www7b.biglobe.ne.jp/~chi-tan/shimotsushima.html

61   県内自衛隊施設数量の詳細」 長崎平和委員会 ['Details of SDF Facilities in Nagasaki Prefecture'], 31 March 2003, at www1.linkclub.or.jp/~chi-tan/nsdf022.html

62   'Coastal Monitoring Field Training', at www1.linkclub.or.jp/~chi-tan/gozaki.html;[郷崎沿岸監視訓練場] in 「所管換協議書」ながさき平和委員会　情報開示請求文書第４９号 ['Jurisdiction Conversion Consultation Document'], Nagasaki Peace Committee, Information Disclosure Request Document No. 49, at www7b.biglobe.ne.jp/~chi-tan/gozaki.html; 「下対馬警備所」、長崎平和委員会 ['Shimotsushima Guard Station', Nagasaki Peace Committee], at www7b.biglobe.ne.jp/~chi-tan/shimotsushima.html; 「県内自衛隊施設数は１６９，件数は減少したが機能は強化」 ['SDF Facilities in the Prefecture Decline to 169, but Their Functions are Enhanced', *Nagasaki Peace Committee News*], 2 October 2002, at www7b.biglobe.ne.jp/~chi-tan/news/news021019.html; 「県内自衛隊施設数量の詳細」、長崎平和委員会 ['Details of SDF Facilities in the Nagasaki Prefecture', *Nagasaki Peace Committee News*], 31 March 2001, at www7b.biglobe.ne.jp/~chi-tan/nsdf002.html; 「陸自郷崎訓練場が拡張へ」、長崎平和委員会 ['GSDF Gozaki Training Station is to Expand', *Nagasaki Peace Committee News*], 21 February 2002, at www7b.biglobe.ne.jp/~chi-tan/news/news020221.html

and submarines of neighbouring countries, information about Japan's acoustic monitoring system, the seabed facilities of the Japan–Korea Strait', and the sound and magnetic signatures of Chinese, North Korean and Russian submarines.[63]

According to a Russian account:

> [The officer] served in a secret technical department on the strategically important islands of Tsushima. The department, in close cooperation with the US, maintains the SOSUS system.
>
> SOSUS is a network of sensors and sonars at the bottom of the Korea Strait where Russian, Chinese, and North Korean ships and submarines very often pass. The system records the noises they produce, and makes a friend–foe distinction. Such data might be very useful in planning military and intelligence operations. The data is jointly shared by armed forces of the US and Japan …
>
> Japanese and American special technical services began making changes to the SOSUS system, suspecting some of its characteristics became known to China.[64]

Wakamiya, Iki Island

Iki Island lies between Kyushu and the Tsushima Islands, in the eastern channel of the Korea Strait. It is 50 kilometres from Shimo-tsushima at the southern end of Tsushima Island, and 16 kilometres across the Iki Strait from north-west Kyushu. The JMSDF station is located at Katsumoto on Wakamiya Island, a small outcrop off the north-west shore of Iki Island. It monitors both surface vessels and submarines passing through the Tsushima Strait.[65]

Iki has been regarded as a 'keystone' of the defence of southern Japan for many centuries. As with Tsushima Island, Iki Island was a founding base of the *Sakimori* frontier guards established in the 7th century to provide defence against Chinese and Korean invaders;[66] its guards featured in the battles against

---

63 'MSDF Officer Quizzed Over China Trips: Petty Officer had Classified Information on Foreign Military Vessels at Home', *Yomiuri Shimbun*, 2 August 2006, at www.yomiuri.co.jp/dy/national/20060802TDY02011. htm; 'New Scandal Erupts at MSDF', *Asahi Shimbun*, 3 August 2006, at www.asahi.com/english/Herald-asahi/TKY200608030062.html; Ren Zihui, 'Japanese Self Defense Force Officer Suspected of Divulging Secrets', *Epoch Times*, 4 August 2006, at www.theepochtimes.com/news/6-8-4/44611.html
64 'Japan Discovers Noise Leakage', *Kommersant*, 3 August 2006, at kommersant.com/page. asp?idr=1&id=694770
65 「壱岐警備所」長崎平和会 ['Iki Guard Station', Nagasaki Peace Committee], at www7b.biglobe. ne.jp/~chi-tan/iki.html
66 Batten, 'The Founding of Dazaifu', at www.fukuokahistory.com/live/content/view/15/52/; Ono Yasumaru, 'Preface to the Chronicle "Kojiki"', at www.geocities.jp/general_sasaki/oono-yasu-eng.html

the Mongol invaders in the 13th century[67] and it was a major base of the *Wakou* pirates who raided China and Korea in the 13th and 14th centuries.[68] In 1641, in the Edo period, a watch post and lighthouse were installed at Wakamiya by the Hirado Domain, having closed the area to foreign traders following rebellions by Japanese Christians encouraged by contesting Dutch, Spanish and Portuguese missionaries. Around 1942, or soon after Japan entered the Second World War, Iki Fortress Command was established, with 15-centimetre artillery emplacements, to strengthen the defences of the Tsushima Strait.

The modern history of the Iki station began in March 1963, when the Iki Guard Unit was officially established as a section of the Sasebo Regional District HQ. Construction of the HQ building and barracks at Wakamiya was completed in April 1963. The unit became operational in October 1963, at which time it had 21 personnel. It was named the Iki Guard Station in 1966. In March 1970, new command arrangements were instituted whereby it was subordinated to the Tsushima Coastal Defense Group HQ at Mitsushima. It has cooperated closely with the Shimo-tsushima Guard Station since the latter became operational in 1969–70. An LQO-3 array was presumably installed at around this time. 'Brand new' barracks were built at the station in the late 1990s.[69]

The operations area consists of two, two-storey buildings. Photographs taken in October 2005 show two hemispherical ESM radomes on the top of the buildings, as well as a VHF antenna and several other antenna systems (see Plate 21).[70]

A JCG facility, with a lighthouse and a HF ground-plane antenna (which transmits on a frequency of 1670.5 kilohertz (KHz)), is located directly above the JMSDF station. Located on its premises is a tower with five microwave dishes mounted on the sides and a platform with four VHF antennas. A smaller tower with another microwave dish is situated nearby.[71]

Another tower with four microwave dishes is located in the middle of Wakamiya Island, on a mountain top above the new barracks. Two of the dishes are directed at Tsushima Island. The other two point towards Sasebo.[72]

---

67 Storry, *A History of Modern Japan*, p. 40; Kennedy, *A Short History of Japan*, pp. 59–60.
68 'Wokou', Wikipedia, at en.wikipedia.org/wiki/Wokou; 'Iki Island', Wikipedia, at wikipedia.org/wiki/Iki_Island
69 「壱岐警備所」長崎平和会 ['Iki Guard Station', Nagasaki Peace Committee], at www7b.biglobe. ne.jp/~chi-tan/iki.html
70 「日本の端（岬 / 灯台）- 8」、『のんびりし』「 ['The Edge of Japan (Capes and Lighthouses)', Part 8], at charider.cside2.com/Nonbiri/nihon/edge8.html
71 'Iki Patrol Base', at www6.kaiho.mlit.go.jp/fukuoka/kisyou/wakamiya/wakamiya2.htm
72 「壱岐警備所」長崎平和会 ['Iki Guard Station', Nagasaki Peace Committee], at www7b.biglobe. ne.jp/~chi-tan/iki.html

Kogozaki Coastal Defense Station

Kogozaki is located near Tarawagaura, on the northern side of the narrow entrance to Sasebo Bay and through to Omura Bay. It was previously an Imperial navy base and, indeed, traces its defence history back to 1714 in the Edo period. The base was taken over by the US Navy in September 1945. A defensive anti-submarine net was laid during the Korean War to monitor and prevent submarine entry into Sasebo harbour. On 2 December 1957, the United States agreed to provide the JMSDF with equipment for installation at both Kogozaki and Kannon Zaki, and a JMSDF post at Kogozaki was established on 16 May 1958. It was officially opened by the JMSDF as Kogozaki Coastal Defense Station in March 1959, and for the next decade was jointly operated with the US Navy. It was transferred to the JMSDF in May 1969. The station was closed in June 1990, but the buildings were maintained for close to another decade. The operations building had a large windowed visual observation deck, with several antennas on the roof; other antennas were mounted on masts and a tower nearby.[73]

By the early 2000s, however, the buildings had fallen into disrepair. Photographs taken in October 2009 show that all the monitoring equipment had been removed and the rooms were littered with rubbish, but the desks, bookshelves, electrical fittings and antennas were still in place.[74] (When the site was visited in October 2010, the access road was overgrown and it was impossible to reach by car and extremely difficult even by foot.)

On the other hand, situated on the south-western side of the old operations building is a remotely controlled oceanographic navigation system for monitoring surface and submarine traffic in the Hario Strait, which, at just 260 metres wide, is the entrance to Sasebo Bay and Omura Bay.[75] The system, produced by the Zeni Lite Buoy Company and installed in 1993, is operated by the Regional Coast Guard's Unit No. 7 (see Plate 22).[76] Hydrophones are moored to the floor of the

73 「向後崎警備所」長崎平和会 ['Kogozaki Guard Station', Nagaski Peace Committee], at www7b. biglobe.ne.jp/~chi-tan/kogozaki.html; 「掃海部隊の歴史」、掃海隊群、海上自衛隊 ['History of Mine-Sweeper Units', Mine-Sweeper Group, JMSDF], at www.mod.go.jp/msdf/mf/history/index.html
74 'JMSDF 監視所 Part 1 – Abandoned Buildings to Monitor the Intruder', 29 November 2009; 'JMSDF 監視所 Part 2 – Ruins of Black and White Photos', 29 November 2009; and 'JMSDF 監視所 Part 3 – Maritime Self-Defense Monitoring Station was Abandoned', 6 December 2009, Forbidden Kyushu, at forbiddenkyushu.wordpress.com/category/%E5%BB%83%E5%A2%9F/jmsdf%E7%9B%A3%E8%A6%96%E6%89%80/
75 「俵ケ浦半島　向後崎灯台と船番所」、つぐみの笑顔 ['Tawaragauru Peninsula, Ship Guard Station and Kogozaki Lighthouse', Smile of the Thrush], 16 March 2012, at blogs.yahoo.co.jp/yamamuraren/archive/2012/03/16
76 Zeni Lite Buoy Company, 'Company Events, Fiscal Year 1993', at www.zenilite.co.jp/topics/p14.html

narrow strait. A 'wide-field camera' attached to the shore facility photographs all surface vessels transiting the strait, while the hydrophones detect and identify the sources of underwater sounds.[77]

White Beach, Okinawa

The JMSDF's Okinawa Ocean Observation Station is located at the White Beach Naval Facility in Katsuren, in Uruma City, on the eastern side of Okinawa Island. The White Beach base was transferred from the US Navy to the JMSDF in 1973, although the US Navy has retained use of its facilities. The Ocean Observation Station, maintained by the JMSDF's Oceanographic Command, reportedly has a SOSUS array, moored 'several hundred km' from the station.[78] An observation/surveillance building at the base, which flies both the Japanese and US flags, has a large visual observation room, with a marine search radar and several other antennas on the roof. A 7-metre diameter radome, mounted on top of a 15-metre high tower, is situated on the hill above the base. It presumably contains radar and/or ELINT equipment.

The small White Beach base, with little berthing space, is usually visited by the US Navy's ocean surveillance/SURTASS ships whenever they are operating in the area. These visits were infrequent, occuring once or twice each year, until 2007, when the rate increased markedly and, by the end of the year, began to happen monthly. For example, the *Victorious* (T-AGOS 19) visited in August and October 2004, and again in February 2008.[79] The *Loyal* (T-AGOS 22) visited in April 2007, August 2007, December 2007 and again in January 2008.[80] The *Impeccable* (T-AGOS 23), the newest of the US Navy's five SURTASS ships, and

77 See, for example, Motonobu Imasato, Nobuo Kiriya, Hiroshi Asou, Osamu Toyama & Kuniyuki Matsushita, 'Development of Marine Surveillance Technology by Sensing Underwater Sound', *Journal of the Japan Institute of Marine Engineering (JIME)* (Vol. 46, No. 1), 2011, at www.mesj.or.jp/publication/award_paper/ap_papers/pdf/2011AP3.pdf
78 「沖縄海洋観測所」、地球探検の旅 ['Okinawa Ocean Observatory' Journey to Explore the Earth], 19 February 2008, at earthjp.net/mercury/0802190004.html; 「沖縄基地」 ['Okinawa Bases'], Wikipedia – Japanese, at ja.wikipedia.org/wiki/%E6%B2%96%E7%B8%84%E5%9F%BA%E5%9C%B0
79 「音響測定艦がもう一隻いた ― ビクトリアス、ホワイトビーチに寄港」 ['One Acoustic Measurement Ship, and then Another – Victorious Enters White Beach'], Rimpeace, 18 January 2008, at www.rimpeace.or.jp/jrp/okinawa/041124wb.html
80 音響測定艦、駆逐艦、揚陸艦がWBに同時入港」 ['Acoustic Measurement Ship, Destroyer, Landing Ship Simultaneously Enter Port at White Beach'], Rimpeace, 13 April 2008, at www.rimpeace.or.jp/jrp/okinawa/080413wb.html; 「音響測定艦ロイヤル、ホワイトビーチに寄港」 ['Acoustic Measurement Ship Royal Enters White Beach'], Rimpeace, 18 January 2008, at www.rimpeace.or.jp/jrp/okinawa/070815loyal.htm; 「音響測定艦、那覇軍港に交代寄港」 ['Acoustic Measurement Ships Alternate Calls at Naha Port'], Rimpeace, 22 July 2007, at www.rimpeace.or.jp/jrp/okinawa/0712tagosnaha.html

the first to be equipped with a low-frequency active (LFA) system, visited in October 2007 and then joined the *Loyal* at White Beach in January 2008.[81] The *Effective* (T-AGOS 21) visited in March and in April 2008.[82]

There is compelling evidence that a new SOSUS array was laid by the US Navy from Kyushu to Okinawa, and connected to White Beach, in 2006. In late 2004, the US Navy's cable-laying ship, the *Zeus* T-ARC 7, began operating in the waters between Kyushu and Okinawa; it visited Sasebo in October, November and December 2004.[83] Then, from January through December 2006, it visited Sasebo 13 times, operating closely with five US Navy oceanographic surveying ships (*Bowditch*, *Bruce C. Heezen*, *John McDonnell*, *Mary Sears* and *Sumner*), and with 10 Los Angeles-class nuclear-powered attack submarines (SSNs), according to records of their port calls to Sasebo and White Beach. Rimpeace, the group of Japanese base-watchers which catalogued the coincidental arrival and departure dates of these vessels at Sasebo and White Beach, stated that the US Navy had previously maintained a SOSUS system around Okinawa to monitor Soviet submarines, but that it had been 'shut down' after the end of the Cold War due to its high operational costs. It argued that the new system is intended to monitor Chinese Navy movements into the Pacific Ocean.[84]

81　「音響測定艦の主な活動海域」['Areas of Acoustic Measurement Ship's Main Activities'] Rimpeace, 21 December 2007, at www.rimpeace.or.jp/jrp/umi/northd/lfaoperation.htm;「ＬＦＡソナー搭載艦２隻、那覇軍港に同時寄港」['Two LFA Sonar-equipped Ships in Simultaneous Call at Naha Naval Base'], at www.rimpeace.or.jp/jrp/okinawa/080123lfalfa.html
82　「音響測定艦エフェクティブ、ＷＢに短時間寄港」['Acoustic Measurement Ship "Effective" Calls Briefly at White Beach'], at www.rimpeace.or.jp/jrp/okinawa/080314effective.html;「音響測定艦エフェクティブ、那覇、ＷＢに連続寄港」['Acoustic Measurement Ship in Continuous Port Calls at Naha and White Bay'], Rimpeace, 13 April 2008, at www.rimpeace.or.jp/jrp/okinawa/080407tagos21.html
83　「ケーブル敷設艦・測量艦の佐世保入港増加の意味は？」['What is the Significance of Increased Port Visits by Cable-laying Ships and Surveying Ships?'], at www.rimpeace.or.jp/jrp/sasebo/sasebobase/0608ssbzeusags.html
84　ibid.

10. Airborne Ocean Surveillance

The Imperial Japanese Navy (IJN) recognised the utility of aircraft for naval reconnaissance during the First World War, using seaplanes for search missions and, in the 1930s, emphasised the importance of aerial scouting in connection with its emerging doctrine of a first strike against enemy carriers.[1] Naval aviation was revived in the 1950s under US direction and, in the late 1950s, the United States agreed to the Japanese Maritime Self-Defense Force's (JMSDF) acquisition of Lockheed P2V-R Neptune anti-submarine warfare (ASW)/ocean patrol aircraft. Kawasaki assembled 48 P2V-Rs at its Gifu plant from 1959 through the early 1960s.[2]

In 1963, Kawasaki initiated a program to convert the P2V-Rs into P–2Js, a radically new Neptune variant that was produced with turboprop engines, an extended fuselage to accommodate 'improved electronic equipment', and an APS-80 search radar, then being installed on the US Navy's new P-3C *Orion* long-range maritime patrol (LRMP) aircraft, to replace the APS-20. The first P-2J was delivered to the JMSDF in November 1966. A total of 83 were built by Kawasaki, the last of which was delivered to the Japanese Maritime Self-Defense Force (JMSDF) in March 1979.[3] The main P-2J operating base was at Hachinohe, in the north-east part of Honshu, with patrol squadrons at Kanoya, in Kagoshima Prefecture, in the southern part of Kyushu, and at Naha in Okinawa. Four squadrons with 40 P-2Js were operational in 1988, three with 30 in 1989–91, and one squadron with only six aircraft in 1993. They had all been phased out by 1994.[4]

The P-2Js were complemented by HSS-2A/B Sea King shore-based ASW patrol helicopters, 185 of which were manufactured by Mitsubishi Heavy Industries, under licence to Sikorsky, in 1989–90.[5] Sixty Sea Kings were deployed with six squadrons (including one for training), with 10 helicopters per squadron, and another 45 kept in store.[6] They were all taken out of service in the late 1990s, although some are still maintained at the JMSDF's air base at Tateyama, at the southern tip of Chiba Prefecture, on the south-eastern side of the entrance to Tokyo Bay, where they are brought out for display during the base's annual air show.

---

1   Evans & Peattie, *Kaigun*, p. 329.
2   Auer, *Postwar Rearmament*, pp. 240–41; 'P2V-7/P-2H', at p2vneptune.com/v07.shtml
3   'Kawasaki P-2J', at p2vneptune.com/v08.shtml
4   IISS, *The Military Balance*.
5   Mark Lambert (ed.), *Jane's All the World's Aircraft 1990–91* (Jane's Information Group, Coulsdon, Surrey, 81st edn, 1990), p. 181.
6   IISS, *The Military Balance 1989–1990* (London, 1989), p. 163.

The P-2Js were replaced through the 1980s and 1990s by P-3C Orions. Acquisition of the P-3Cs was approved by the Cabinet in December 1978. The first three of these were produced by Lockheed in the United States and handed over to the JMSDF in April 1981. The next four were assembled by Kawasaki at Gifu, using parts manufactured by Lockheed, in 1982. Another 100 were produced by Kawasaki, including about a dozen variants for 'special missions', such as the EP-3s and UP-3s. By March 1990, 60 had been delivered, and all of them by 1995. The P-3C is still recognised as the best ASW and maritime surveillance system in the world. It is a four-engined aircraft capable of flying 2,500 kilometres with full weapons load, patrolling for four hours, and returning to base. It is equipped with a variety of submarine detection systems, including sonobuoys, an infra-red detection system, an AN/ASQ-81 magnetic anomaly detection (MAD) system, two AN/ARR-78 sonar receivers, and two AN/AQA-7(V)8 DIFAR (directional acoustic frequency analysis and recording) sonobuoy sets, as well as an AN/APS-115 search radar (with 360° coverage), and advanced navigation and communications (including satellite communication (Satcom)) systems. It also carries an AN/ALQ-78 electronic countermeasures (ECM) set and an AN/ALR-66(V)3 electronic support measures (ESM) system for self-defence.[7]

The JMSDF currently has more than 80 P-3C Orions in service. They are deployed with eight squadrons, each with 10 aircraft, plus a small number with the 51st Training and Development Squadron at Atsugi, south of Tokyo. Two squadrons, the 31st and 32nd Air Patrol Squadrons, are based under the 3rd Fleet Air Wing at Atsugi. The 21st and 22nd, part of the 2nd Fleet Air Wing, are based at Hachinohe; the 11th and 12th, part of the 1st Fleet Air Wing, are based at Kanoya; and the 51st and 52nd Squadrons are part of the 5th Fleet Air Wing based at Naha. Fleet Squadron 81 of the 31st Fleet Air Wing, based at Iwakuni, operates five EP-3C SIGINT aircraft (Nos. 9171–9175), which are used for both national and JMSDF SIGINT collection activities (see Table 2).

Table 2. JMSDF maritime patrol aircraft bases

Base	Squadron	Aircraft
Atsugi (Fleet Air Wing 4)	Fleet Squadron 3	P-3C
	Fleet Squadron 6	P-3C
	Fleet Squadron 51 (Air Development Squadron)	P-3C, UP-3C, UP-3D, SH-60J
Kanoya (Fleet Air Wing 1)	Fleet Squadron 1	P-3C
	Fleet Squadron 7	P-3C

---

7   Paul Jackson (ed.), *Jane's All the World's Aircraft 1997–98*, (Jane's Information Group, Coulsdon, Surrey, 88th edn, 1997), pp. 289–90.

Hachinohe (Fleet Air Wing 2)	Fleet Squadron 2	P-3C
	Fleet Squadron 4	P-3C
Naha (Fleet Air Wing 5)	Fleet Squadron 5	P-3C
	Fleet Squadron 9	P-3C
Iwakuni (Fleet Air Wing 31)	Fleet Squadron 81	EP-3C
Tateyama (Fleet Air Wing 21)	Fleet Squadron 101	SH-60J
	Fleet Squadron 121	SH-60J
	Fleet Squadron 123	SH-60J
Omura (Fleet Air Wing 22)	Fleet Squadron 122	SH-60J
	Fleet Squadron 124	SH-60J

The Naha squadrons with their 20 P-3Cs are commonly reckoned to be the busiest of the JMSDF's P-3C squadrons, as well as operating in the tensest area. They make daily flights over the Senkaku Islands and surrounding waters.[8] Mission data is transmitted directly from P-3Cs in-flight to the JMSDF's Kunigami Receiving Station located in dense forest about 3 kilometres east of Iji village in Kunigami District in northern Okinawa. The requirement for an 'aviation anti-submarine warfare centre and communications facility' for the 5th Fleet Air Wing was announced by the JMSDF in August 1988. Construction began at the Kunigami site in November 1990, and was completed in September 1991. The station occupies 560 square metres, and consists of a large operations building, a 7-element circular HF array (with one of the masts in the centre, the outer masts forming a 63-metre diameter array on a circular 85-metre diameter pad), a 6-element circular HF array (with the masts forming a 43-metre diameter array on an 80-metre diameter circular pad), a microwave tower with two microwave dishes, pointing to Naha, a HF wire antenna string between two steel masts, and a large log-periodic array (LPA) on a steel tower about 300 metres west-north-west of the 7-element array.[9] The antennas are clearly shown in high-resolution Google Earth imagery dated 18 January 2013. An optical fibre cable runs along the roadside between the station and Iji village.

In November 2001, Kawasaki was contracted to design and produce an indigenous replacement for the aging P-3Cs. Initially called the P-X, it was redesignated the XP-1 when the first prototype aircraft was rolled out from Kawasaki's Gifu factory in July 2007. It completed its maiden flight in September 2007. The first

---

8 Kyle Mizokami, 'The Mainichi Rides Along with Japan's Senkaku Patrol', *Japan Security Watch*, 17 October 2011, at jsw.newpacificinstitute.org/?p=8524

9 『沖縄県の基地の現状』、沖縄県、沖縄県総務部知事公室, 平成15年3月 ['State of the Bases in Okinawa Prefecture', Public Affairs Office, Governor of Okinawa Prefecture, March 2003], at www.pref.okinawa.jp/kititaisaku/D-mokuji.htm

test aircraft was delivered to the Ministry of Defense (MoD) in August 2008 and another four in March 2010. The first two production models, now called P-1s, were delivered to the JMSDF on 26 March 2013. They were deployed to the Atsugi base to undergo flight tests for two years before beginning maritime patrol missions.[10] The Mid-Term Defense Build-up Plan, which was adopted by the government in December 2010, included the purchase of 10 P-1s within five years 'to monitor submarines and suspicious boats', at a cost of approximately 200 billion yen, or about US$200 million per aircraft.[11]

The P-1 has a length of 38 metres, a wing span of 35 metres, and a maximum weight of about 80,000 kilograms. It is powered by four F7-10 turbofan engines produced by Ishikawajima-Harima Heavy Industries, which provide a cruise speed of 830 kilometres per hour and a maximum speed of 996 kilometres per hour. It travels at about 1.3 times faster than the P-3C, can operate at higher altitudes, and 'can conduct surveillance flights for more than 10 hours'. Because each aircraft can monitor a greater area than a P3-C, the JMSDF expects that it can replace its 80 P-3Cs with 70 P-1s.[12]

It has a flight crew of two and can carry a mission crew of 11 (compared to seven in the P-3C). It is fitted with a MAD boom for submarine detection, and can carry 30 preloaded sonar buoys and another 70 reloads within the aircraft. Its avionics equipment includes a Toshiba HPS-106 active electronically scanned array (AESA) radar, a Fujitsu HAQ-2 forward-looking infra-red (FLIR) system, a HQA-7(NEC)/HAS-107/HRQ-1(JRC)/HQH-106 advanced acoustics suite, a Mitsubishi Electric HLR-109B ESM system, a HYQ-3 Combat Direction System, and a Kawasaki HAS-108 data-link system.[13]

The HSS-2B Sea King helicopters have been succeeded by SH-60J Sea Hawks. Manufactured by Mitsubishi Heavy Industries under licence to Sikorsky, 101 SH-60Js have been delivered to the JMSDF since 1991. The SH-60J is extensively modified compared to the standard Sikorsky/US Navy version, especially with respect to its avionics. The SH-60J retains the US-built Texas Instruments AN/ASQ-81D2 MAD, General Instruments AN/ALR-66 (VE) radar warning receiver (RWR), Ednac AN/ARR-75 sonobuoy receiver and the Raytheon AN/AAS-44 FLIR/laser detection, ranging and tracking system. The indigenous Japanese

---

10 'Kawasaki XP-1 Maritime Patrol Aircraft, Japan', Naval Technology, at www.naval-technology.com/projects/kawasaki-xp-1-maritime-patrol-aircraft/; 'KHI Gives MSDF First P-1 Anti-Sub Aircraft', Japan Times, 27 March 2013.
11 'Japan Will Buy 10 P1 Planes', House of Japan, 18 November 2010, at www.houseofjapan.com/local/japan-will-buy-10-p1-patrol-planes
12 ibid.; 'KHI Gives MSDF First P-1 Anti-Sub Aircraft'.
13 'Kawasaki P-1', at www.heinkel.jp/yspack/ysf_p1_eng.html; 'Kawasaki P-1 Database', at harpgamer.com/harpforum/index.php?/topic/17948-kawasaki-p-1/

equipment includes the HPS-104 search radar, HLR-108 ESM system, HQS-103 dipping sonar, cockpit displays, tactical data processor and data links. It has an operational range of about 1,000 kilometres.[14]

The JMSDF currently maintains five squadrons of shore-based and four squadrons of shipboard SH-60J helicopters. The shore-based units, which each have 10 helicopters, consist of Fleet Squadrons 101, 121 and 123, based at Tateyama; and Fleet Squadrons 122 and 124, based at Omura, in the north-west part of Kyushu. The 513th unit of the 51st Training and Development Squadron at Atsugi also has a handful of SH-60Js.[15]

Mitsubishi is currently producing an advanced version of the SH-60J, called the SH-60K. A prototype was rolled out in September 2001, and Mitsubishi delivered an initial batch of seven to the JMSDF in 2005. A second batch of 50 is in production. The SH-60K has substantially upgraded avionics, including a data link, and enhanced defensive countermeasures systems, including a missile warning system and a chaff dispenser.[16]

JMSDF ELINT Processing and Correlation Centres

Electronic intelligence (ELINT) collected by the JMSDF's EP-3 SIGINT aircraft is delivered to the Electronic Data Analysis Department at their home base at Iwakuni in Yamaguchi Prefecture, for second-echelon processing and analysis. Urgent matters are transmitted directly to the Electronic Intelligence Center (EIC) at the Fleet HQ in Yokosuka, which changed its name from the Electronic Operations Support Unit (EOSU) in 1997, and which provides ELINT support to the Fleet Intelligence Center (FIC) and thence the JMSDF Fleet Command at Yokosuka.[17] For example, when North Korea launched a Taepodong missile over Japan on 31 August 1998, the telemetry signals emitted by the missile were recorded by an EP-3; when the aircraft landed at Iwakuni the tapes were carried by hand to the Electronic Data Analysis Department and the data was 'instantaneously electronically transmitted' by data link to the EOSU at Yokosuka.[18]

---

14   Jackson (ed.), *Jane's All the World's Aircraft 1997–98*, p. 296.
15   'Japanese Fleet', *GlobalSecurity.org*, at www.globalsecurity.org/military/world/japan/jmsdf-orbat.htm
16   'Difference Between SH-60J and SH-60J Kai', at forum.keypublishing.co.uk/archive/index.php?t-47376. html; 'Sikorsky SH-60B "Sea Hawk" 1979', at www.aviastar.org/helicopters_eng/sik_s-70-sea.php
17   *Asagumo* report, undated (but probably 1997), photocopied excerpts.
18   'Japan: State Incapable of Waging War', *Bungei Shinju*, Tokyo, November 1998, pp. 150–57, in FBIS Translated Text, East Asia, FBIS-EAS-98-299, 26 October 1988.

The EIC at Yokosuka collects, correlates, processes and analyses the electronic signals emitted by ships and aircraft and intercepted by the JMSDF's ship-borne, airborne and shore-based ELINT systems. The mission of the FIC, which had about 200 personnel in the late 1990s, is to collect and analyse the operational intelligence required for the operations of JMSDF forward units and to provide related units with that intelligence. It receives intelligence from the Basic Intelligence Center (BIC) at the Defense Intelligence Headquarters (DIH) at Ichigaya and the Operational Intelligence Center (OIC) at Yokosuka as well as from the EIC.[19]

---

19 *Asagumo* report.

11. JMSDF SIGINT Collection and Ocean Surveillance Ships

The Japanese Maritime Self-Defense Force (JMSDF) has a small fleet of 'oceanographic survey and research vessels' and other auxiliary vessels that it uses for varied ocean surveillance activities. The fleet includes three ships that are equipped for signals intelligence (SIGINT) collection activities (the *Nichinan* AGS/AGI 5105 and the *Shonan* AGS 5106, operated by the Oceanographic Command HQ at Yokosuka, and the *Shirase* AGB/AGI 5003 polar icebreaker) and two Surveillance Towed Array Sensor System (SURTASS) ocean surveillance ships (the *Hibiki* AOS 5201 and the *Harima* AOS 5202) operated by the Fleet Intelligence Command (FIC) (see Table 3).

The JMSDF's first ship configured for SIGINT collection was the *Akashi* (AGS/AGI 5101), built by the Nippon Steel Tube Company at Tsurumi, near Yokohama, where it was laid down in September 1968, launched in May 1969, and commissioned in October 1969. It had a length of 74 metres, a displacement of 1,420 tons, and a range of 26,500 kilometres (at 14 knots), with a crew of 75 (including about 10 SIGINT technicians). It had 'a large number of electronic intercept aerials', including a NEC NOLR–6 ESM system for radar intercepts. It was withdrawn from service and replaced by the *Nichinan* in 1999.[1]

The *Nichinan* AGS/AGI 5105 was planned in 1996, laid down in August 1997, launched in June 1998, and commissioned in March 1999. Built by Mitsubishi at its Shimonoseki shipyards, it has a length of 111 metres and a displacement of 3,300 tons, and a complement of 80.[2] In order to 'improve its observation capability', it has an electric propulsion system which produces less noise, in addition to its main diesel engines. Its equipment includes an 'ocean observation system', a towed side-sonar array, sonobuoys, and a remotely operated vehicle (ROV).[3] It also has a dynamic positioning system (DPS) to automatically keep the ship at a fixed position.[4]

The *Nichinan*'s activities are usually unannounced and unreported. On 10 February 2006, however, the JMSDF issued a press release saying that the *Nichinan* was conducting surveys of the continental shelf south of Kyushu. It stated that: 'The survey is proceeding, but this announcement is an unusual

---

1   Richard Sharpe (ed.), *Jane's Fighting Ships 1996–97* (Jane's Information Group, Coulsdon, Surrey, 99th edn, 1996), p. 383.
2   Richard Sharpe (ed.), *Jane's Fighting Ships 2000–2001* (Jane's Information Group, Coulsdon, Surrey, 103rd edn, 2000), p. 385.
3   'AGS Nichinan Class', *GlobalSecurity.org*, at www.globalsecurity.org/military/world/japan/nichinan.htm
4   'Dynamic Positioning System', 三井造船 [Mitsui Engineering & Shipbuilding] at www.mes.co.jp/english/business/ship/ship_11.html

exception in the usually highly secret activities of the ocean observation ship'. It said that the survey work would continue until early March. Other official sources said that the *Nichinan* had conducted similar survey work in the area in January–February 2005. The surveys had been mandated by a 'Meeting of Relevant Ministers and Agencies on Continental Shelf Survey and Marine Resources', in order to demarcate the continental shelf following the intrusions of Chinese 'observation' and marine survey ships inside Japan's claimed exclusive economic zone (EEZ) in 2004–05.[5]

Table 3. JMSDF ocean surveillance ships

Name	Designation	Type	Commissioned
1. Nichinan	AGS/AGI-5105	Ocean Survey	1999
2. Shonan	AGS-5106	Ocean Survey	2011
3. Suma	AGS-5103	Ocean Survey	1982
4. Futami	AGS-5102	Ocean Survey	1979
5. Wakasa	AGS-5104	Ocean Survey	1986
6. Shirase	AGB-5003	Icebreaker	2009
7. Hibiki	AOS-5201	SURTASS	1991
8. Harima	AOS-5202	SURTASS	1992

The *Nichinan*'s activities gained media attention again in January 2014, when it was reported that it had lost its ROV when the cables connecting the device with the ship broke on 30 November 2013 while it was operating in the Tsugaru Strait. A Ministry of Defense (MoD) official stated on 29 January that the ROV 'was being used to survey the underwater terrain as well as water currents and temperatures' in the strait. Press reports noted that such data was used 'to track the movements of foreign submarines nearby'.[6] A Chinese report identified the

5 JMSDF, '"Nichinan" Carrying Out Continental Shelf Survey', 10 February 2006, at jmsdf.sakura.ne.jp/news/c-news/18/021002.htm; 「海洋観測艦「にちなん」の活動について 17．1．21 (海上自衛隊海上幕僚監部)」，徒然日記「多事某論」保管庫 ['Activities of the Ocean Surveillance Ship "Nichinan", 21 January 2005 (JMSDF Maritime Staff Office)', 'At a Loose End Diary: "A Certain Theory about Many Events"'], 25 January 2005, at bosc1945.exblog.jp/1844865
6 'MSDF Admits Losing Submersible in Tsugaru Strait', *Japan Times*, 29 January 2014, at www.japantimes.co.jp/news/2014/01/29/national/msdf-admits-losing-submersible-in-tsugaru-strait/; 'MSDF Unmanned Survey Device Lost at Sea after Cable Severed', *Kyodo News International*, 29 January 2014, at www.globalpost.com/dispatch/news/kyodo-news-international/140129/msdf-unmanned-survey-device-lost-at-sea-after-cable-se

ROV as an SCV-3000, which measured 3 metres in length, 1.7 metres in height and 1.7 metres in width, weighed four tons, and was 'equipped with cameras and sonar detectors'; it said that the JMSDF needed improved oceanographic data because China's submarines had become quieter in recent years.[7] The MoD, Itsunori Onodera, stated on 31 January that the 'underwater survey was resumed using one of the other ROVs the MSDF possesses'.[8]

The *Shonan* AGS 5106 was authorised in FY 2006, laid down in December 2008, launched in June 2009, completed in March 2010 and commissioned in March 2011. It was built by the Mitsui Engineering and Shipbuilding Company at Tamano in Okayama Prefecture. It has a length of 103 metres and a width of 16.4 metres and a standard displacement of 3,200 tonnes or 4,150 tonnes with a full load. It is capable of a speed of 16 knots, and carries a crew of 80.[9] It is home ported, together with the *Nichinan*, at Yokosuka.[10]

In addition to the *Nichinan* and the *Shonan*, the Oceanographic Command currently has three other ocean survey and research ships: the *Suma* AGS 5103 coastal survey ship, which became operational in 1982; and the *Futami* AGS 5102 and *Wakasa* AGS 5104 oceanographic research ships, which became operational in 1979 and 1986 and are 'fitted for hydrographic survey and cable laying', and which carry RCV-225 remote-controlled underwater survey submarines.[11]

The JMSDF has also had two successive polar icebreakers equipped for communications intelligence (COMINT) and electronic intelligence (ELINT) collection – the *Fuji* AGB/AGI 5001 (1965–83) and the *Shirase* AGB/AGI 5002 (1982–2007). They typically operated in the Antarctic for several months each year during the northern summer, but operated in the area north of Hokkaido in the winter, when these waters are covered with thick ice and inaccessible to the primary Auxiliary General Intelligence (AGI) ship. The *Fuji* was built by Nippon Steel Tube Company at Tsurumi, and was commissioned in July 1965. It was 100 metres long and had a normal displacement of 7,760 tons, and was equipped with a large horizontal HF log-periodic antenna, navigation and weather radars, an SQS-11A sonar system, a HF DF crossed-loop antenna system, a NIPRORI-1 sea gravimeter system, three helicopters, and carried a crew of 200 plus 35 'scientists and observers'.[12]

---

7   'SDF Lost Influence Underwater Robot Submarine Reconnaissance China', 29 January 2014, at www. wantinews.com/news-6326393-SDF-lost-influence-underwater-robot-submarine-reconnaissance-China.html

8   'Press Conference by the Defense Minister Onodera', Ministry of Defense, 31 January 2014, at www.mod. go.jp/e/pressconf/2014/01/140131.html

9   'Shonan Class Ocean Survey Ship', *JMSDF Vessels*, at homepage2.nifty.com/nishidah/e/dtc0635.htm

10   Captain Sato, 'Activities of Oceanographic Command JMSDF', 10 February 2012, at www.rioe.or.jp/ mts20120210_3.pdf

11   Andrew Toppan, 'World Navies Today: Japan', 23 May 2002, at www.hazegray.org/worldnav/asiapac/ japan.htm; Sharpe (ed.), *Jane's Fighting Ships 2000–2001*, p. 386.

12   John Moore (ed.), *Jane's Fighting Ships 1982–83* (Jane's Publishing Company, London, 85th edn, 1982), p. 270; Sagawa Jiro, Kaminuma Katsutada and Ueda Yoshio, 'Sea Gravimeter System of the Icebreaker "SHIRASE"',

The *Fuji* was replaced by the *Shirase* AGB/AGI 5002 in 1983. It was also built by Nippon Steel Tube Company at Tsurumi; it was laid down in March 1981, launched in December 1981, and commissioned in November 1982. It was 134 metres long, and had a displacement of 11,600 tonnes. It had a crew of 170, and could carry 60 'scientists and observers', and was 'fully equipped for marine and atmospheric research'. Its equipment included a JRC OPS-18-1 G-band surface search radar, an OPS-22 I-band navigation radar, two electronic support measures (ESM) systems, a HF DF crossed-loop antenna, a weather radar in a large radome, 'various ocean observation units', and three helicopters.[13] The NIPRORI-1 sea gravimeter system was transferred from the *Fuji*, but improvements to enhance its capabilities were incorporated in the process, including installation of a larger data processing unit and improved software for data processing.[14] The *Shirase* (AGB 5002) was decommissioned in April 2007. Its successor, also named *Shirase* (AGB 5003), became operational in November 2009.[15]

The JMSDF's two SURTASS or 'acoustic measurement ships', the *Hibiki* AOS 5201 and the *Harima* AOS 5202, also called J-AOS (Japanese Auxiliary Oceanographic System) ships, became operational in 1991 and 1992. The JMSDF had initially planned to procure five SURTASS ships, but the program was truncated with the end of the Cold War. The ships were built at the Mitsui shipyard in Tamano. They have a crew of 40, and are both home ported at Kure.[16]

Construction of the *Hibiki* AOS 5201 was authorised on 24 January 1989; it was launched in July 1990 and commissioned in January 1991. It then sailed to the United States for installation of the UQQ-2 SURTASS array.[17] Called the NQQ-2 in Japan, the passive array is towed by a 1,830-metre-long cable when in deep water, or as a 'twin-line towed array' with two shorter (800-metre) cables when operating in shallow water.[18]

Memoirs of National Institute of Polar Research, September 1984, at http://ci.nii.ac.jp/naid/110000009895/en/

13   Sharpe (ed.), *Jane's Fighting Ships 2000–2001*, p. 386; JMSDF, '"Shirase" AGB 5002', at www.mod.go.jp/msdf/formal/gallery/ships/agb/index.html

14   Sagawa Jiro, Kaminuma Katsutada and Ueda Yoshio, 'Sea Gravimeter System of the Icebreaker "SHIRASE"', at ci.nii.ac.jp/naid/110000009895/en/

15   'Icebreaker Shirase Bids Farewell to Antarctica', 15 February 2007, at www.breitbart.com/print.php?id=D8UR5GE00&show_article=1; 'Point of View. Katsutada Kaminuma: Icebreaker Shirase Still Good for Another Year', *Asahi Shimbun*, 11 March 2007, at www.asahi.com/english/Herald-asahi/TKY200711030051.html; '新南極観測船「しらせ」', 日本マリンエンジニアリング学会誌 第45巻 第2号 (2010) ['New Antarctic Research Ship', *Journal of the Japan Institute of Marine* Engineering, (Vol. 45, No. 2), 2010], pp. 32–37, at www.jstage.jst.go.jp/article/jime/45/2/45_180/_pdf

16   Friedman, *Naval Institute Guide*, p. 24; 'AOS Hibiki Class', *GlobalSecurity.org*, at www.globalsecurity.org/military/world/japan/hibiki.htm; James Simpson, 'Japan's Ears on the Sea', at medium.com/war-is-boring/japans-ears-on-the-sea-39bf83f0acb7

17   Sharpe (ed.), *Jane's Fighting Ships 2000–2001*, p. 385; 'AOS Hibiki Class', at www.globalsecurity.org/military/world/japan/hibiki.htm; Simpson, Simpson, 'Japan's Ears on the Sea', at medium.com/war-is-boring/japans-ears-on-the-sea-39bf83f0acb7

18   'Acoustic Measurement Ship "HIBIKI" Type', *Vessel and Ships Photo Gallery*, at www.vspg.net/jmsdf/aos-hibiki-class.html

Five US Navy technicians serve aboard each J-AOS ship. According to Norman Friedman, the 'US technical crews … operate the sensors', and 'Japan and the United States share their surveillance data'.[19]

Both the J-AOS ships were included in a major 'block upgrade' of the US Navy's SURTASS ships in 1997–98. The capabilities of the passive acoustic data collection and analysis system were expanded by adding a reduced diameter array (RDA) and a commercial off-the-shelf (COTS) processing system to 'provide increased detection capability, more flexible and higher resolution spectrum analysis, and improved target bearing'. The communications system was also upgraded to provide additional UHF satellite communications (Satcom) voice and data connectivity between the SURTASS vessels and 'tactical platforms'.[20]

The 'block upgrade' also added an active adjunct to the towed array, involving a WQT-2 LFA (low-frequency active) system for detection of quieter submarines in shallow and coastal waters. In addition to the 'active transmit array and handling system', the LFA system includes 'power amplification and control systems, an active signal processing and display receive system, and an environmental analysis system'.[21] Hughes also received a contract in February 1998 for 'SURTASS/J-AOS block upgrade system software maintenance'.[22]

Data collected by the SURTASS vessels is sent to a data collection and analysis station at Yokosuka using AN/WSC-6(V)1 satellite communications systems.[23] The WSC-6(V)1 has a 1.22-metre diameter reflector dish in a radome that is 1.57 metres in diameter and 2.16 metres high. The WSC-6(V) uses the US Defense Satellite Communications System (DSCS)-III satellite system; it transmits in the 7.9–8.4 gigahertz band and receives in the 7.25–7.75 gigahertz band.[24]

The JMSDF's Oceanographic Command also maintains a cable-laying and repair ship, which is not only essential for laying and repairing the cables connecting the fixed sea-bottom hydrophone arrays with their respective shore stations, but which also has extensive ocean survey capabilities. For a quarter of a century, this was the *Tsugaru* ARC 481, one of the first products of Japan's postwar domestic ship-building program, which was approved by the United States in 1953. Built by the Yokohama Shipyard, it was laid down in December 1954, launched in July 1955 and became operational in December 1955, and initially

---

19 Friedman, *Guide to World Naval Weapons Systems*, pp. 21, 24; Toppan, 'World Navies Today: Japan', at www.hazegray.org/worldnav/asiapac/japan.htm; 'Japan–US Security Treaty After 50 Years — Phantom Alliance', in American Embassy, Tokyo, 'Daily Summary of Japanese Press', 28 August 2001.

20 'Sensors', *America's Navy*, at www.navy.mil/navydata/policy/vision/vis98/vis-p10.html

21 ibid.

22 US Department of Defense, 'Contracts for Thursday, February 12, 1998', at www.defenselink.mil/contracts/contract.aspx?contractid=1215.

23 Sharpe (ed.), *Jane's Fighting Ships 2000–2001*, p. 385.

24 'AN/WSC-6(V) SHF SATCOM Set', in John Williamson (ed.), *Jane's Military Communications, 1996–97* (Jane's Information Group, Coulsdon, Surrey, 17th edn, 1996), pp. 376–77.

served as a mine layer in addition to its 'main mission ... to lay listening devices' around bases and ports. In a major refit in 1969–70, it was lengthened, widened, and its displacement increased from around 1,000 tons to 2,150 tons. The mine racks were removed, its QHBa sonar was replaced with a more advanced SQS-11A system, and it was converted into a specialised cable-laying ship carrying a crew of approximately 100. It was withdrawn from service in March 1980.[25]

The *Tsugaru* was succeeded by the *Muroto* ARC 482, built by Mitsubishi at its Shimonoseki shipyard. Launched in July 1979 and commissioned in March 1980, it has a length of 133 metres, a displacement of 4,500 tons, and a crew of 135. It has an 'ocean survey capability', as well as a special 'burying system' for hiding or protecting the sea-bottom cables.[26] It is home ported at Kure, but often works out of Ominato or Sasebo. Its activities have been described as 'secrets within a secret'.[27]

The JMSDF also has two experimental ships (ASEs) with extensive electronic surveillance and acoustic capabilities. The *Kurihama* ASE 6101 was built by Sasebo Heavy Industries for the Technical Research and Development Institute (TRDI) 'for testing underwater weapons and sensors'. Launched in September 1979 and commissioned in April 1980, it has a length of 68 metres, displacement of 950 tons, and a crew of 40 plus 12 scientists.[28]

The *Asuka* ASE 6102 'radar and sonar trials ship', operated by the Development and Training Command, is equipped to test and evaluate a variety of electronic surveillance, radar, sonar, and countermeasures systems. Built by Sumitomo Heavy Industries at Uraga, in Yokosuka, and commissioned in March 1995, it has a length of 151 metres and displaces 4,250 tons, a helicopter flight deck, and a complement of 72 plus up to 100 scientists. It is home ported at Yokosuka. It is equipped with an FCS-3 weapons control system, utilising a 'mini-*Aegis*' SPY-1D-type E/F-band air search radar, as well as a Melco OPS-14B D-band air/surface search radar, a JRC OPS-18-1 G-band surface search radar, and a Type 3 I/J-band fire control radar.[29] It is also equipped with an infra-red suppression system (IRSS) produced by Davis/Defence Research Establishment

25   'JMSDF Ships — ARC 481 Tsugaru Class', けいのがらくた置き場 [Kei's Boneyard]), at www2c.airnet. ne.jp/junkyard/jmsdf/ARC481Tsugara.html; 'Japanese Minelayers', at www.battleships-cruisers.co.uk/ japanese_minelayers.htm

26   Sharpe (ed.), *Jane's Fighting Ships 2000–2001*, p. 385; 'ARC Muroto Class', at www.globalsecurity.org/ military/world/japan/muroto.htm

27   Taoka Shunji, 'Sea-lane Defence', *Asahi Shimbun*, 1 May 1984.

28   Sharpe (ed.), *Jane's Fighting Ships 2000–2001*, p. 386.

29   Sharpe (ed.), *Jane's Fighting Ships 2000–2001*, p. 386; Toppan, 'World Navies Today: Japan', at www. hazegray.org/worldnav/asiapac/japan.htm

Suffield (DRES) in Alberta, Canada, and supplied to Sumitomo Heavy Industries in January 1994, for reducing its infra-red signature by cooling the hot metal and gases generated by its gas turbine engines.[30]

30 'IRSS for Japanese Frigate', *Davis Newsletter*, July 1997, at www.wrdavis.com/docs/news/html/07/index.html

12. The US Ocean Surveillance Information System (OSIS)

Both the US Navy's 7th Fleet Command and the Japanese Maritime Self-Defense Force's (JMSDF) Fleet HQ at Yokosuka receive all intelligence of interest from the US Navy's Ocean Surveillance Information System (OSIS), its global network of sound surveillance system (SOSUS) facilities, HF DF stations (called *Classic Bullseye*), ocean surveillance satellites, and ship-based and airborne sensor systems. The OSIS was developed in the 1970s, and focussed on the Soviet navy. It consisted of a Naval Ocean Surveillance Information Center (NOSIC) at Suitland in Maryland; three Fleet Ocean Surveillance Information Centers (FOSIC), located in London, Honolulu, and Norfolk, Virginia; and two Fleet Ocean Surveillance Information Facilities (FOSIF), located at Rota in Spain and at the Naval Support Facility at Kamiseya, some 25 kilometres north-west of Yokosuka. The system was described by one of its progenitors in 1982 as follows:

> The Ocean Surveillance Information System (OSIS) consists of a network of personnel, facilities, computers, communications, and procedures designed to receive, process, correlate, and disseminate evaluated ocean surveillance information. The system provides near real-time, all-source indications and warning, threat assessment, positional and movement information, and over-the-horizon targeting (OTH-T) support to national, theatre and fleet users. Of particular importance is the support provided to fleet users via the Navy Communications System. This support includes daily summaries, spot reporting, event-by-event reporting on selected high-interest targets, and estimates of intentions. It is this ongoing requirement for near real-time evaluated intelligence information on air, surface, and sub-surface platforms that led to OSIS.[1]

The FOSIF in the Western Pacific was the last element to be constructed. Its location was a major issue. According to a former US Navy intelligence officer who was involved in the site selection process in 1971, three areas were initially proposed — California, Guam and Japan: 'Both the San Francisco and San Diego regions of California were investigated, but considered too far from principal areas of surveillance', while 'Guam had the advantage of being US territory, but its communications facilities and available operating spaces were considered secondary to Japan'. Kamiseya was finally selected because of the presence of

---

1   Samuel L. Gravely, Jr., 'OSIS Extends Intelligence Coverage Beyond Radar Horizon', *Defense Electronics*, April 1982, p. 70.

the Naval Security Group's (NSG) large signals intelligence (SIGINT) station and its proximity to Yokosuka. The Kamiseya FOSIF was activated on 15 February 1972.[2]

The NSG SIGINT station at Kamiseya was established in 1952 and, by the 1960s, was its largest station in the world, with more than 1,000 personnel. It had vast antenna fields, with several HF DF systems, including AN/FLR-11 and AN/GRD-6 circularly disposed antenna arrays (CDAA) and two arrays of loop antennas, and it served for two decades as the Pacific HF DF Net Control Station, controlling the network of HF DF stations that stretched across the Pacific from Okinawa to California.[3]

The current OSIS architecture is different from that of the 1970s and the 1980s. Collection systems have changed to reflect changing communications technologies, and especially the move from HF radio to satellite communications. The US Navy's intelligence organisation was drastically reformed after the end of the Cold War; together with new data management and secure dissemination technologies, and this has produced a more streamlined, but also more networked, structure for dissemination of ocean surveillance information.

The original OSIS organisation was reformed in the early 1990s. The FOSICs and FOSIFs were disestablished, and their functions transferred to joint-Service intelligence centres and joint commands, such as the Joint Intelligence Center – Pacific (JICPAC) at US Pacific Command (USPACOM) HQ at Honolulu. The FOSIF WestPac at Kamiseya became JICPAC J-DET on 1 October 1993. J-DET was transferred to Yokosuka, together with other NSG elements, and the NSG station at Kamiseya was closed, with effect from 1 June 1995.[4] The NSG was itself disestablished and replaced by the Information Operations Directorate (IOD) of the Naval Network Warfare Command (NETWARCOM) in September 2005. The NSG's units became Navy Information Operations Commands (NIOCs) or Navy Information Operations Detachments (NIODs). NIOCs were initially located at Misawa and Yokosuka, but the unit at Misawa was disestablished on 30 September 2014.[5]

---

2   Gus Hancock, 'OSIS: Forging the Links', *Naval Intelligence Professionals Quarterly*, Summer 1991, pp. 9–10.

3   Jay R. Browne, 'Early Development', *Cryptolog: U.S. Naval Cryptologic Veterans Association* (Vol. 18, No. 4), Fall 1997, pp. 26–28.

4   Jay R. Browne, 'Kami Seya – The Last Years', *Cryptolog: U.S. Naval Cryptologic Veterans Association* (Vol. 18, No. 4), Fall 1997, pp. 43–47.

5   Jeffrey T. Richelson, *The US Intelligence Community* (Westview, Boulder, Colorado, 5th edn, 2008), pp. 98–99; 'United States Navy Information Operations Command Misawa: Command History', at www. niocmisawa.navy.mil/history.html; 'Naval Security Group Station History Dates', at www.navycthistory. com/NSGStationsHistoryDates.txt; Memorandum from the Chief of Naval Operations, 'Disestablishment of Navy Information Operations Command, Misawa, Japan and Realignment of Navy Information Operations Command Detachment, Seoul, Korea' (OPNAV Notice 5400, 5 September 2014).

On the technical side, the OSIS system was upgraded in the early 1990s through the OSIS Baseline Upgrade (OBU) program. Powerful new computers were installed to serve the workstations at the new joint-Service centres, and the timeliness of the ocean surveillance intelligence was significantly enhanced, with the OSIS database updated 'with each satellite pass and each new sensor reading'.[6] OBU hardware and software was sold to Japan and installed at the JMSDF Fleet HQ at Yokosuka at the same time, together with equipment produced by Mitsubishi and Hitachi.[7] Around 1999, the OBU Evolutionary Development (OED) program was implemented, involving more advanced hardware and software for receiving, processing and disseminating all-source surveillance information in near-real-time. OED systems were installed at JICPAC in Honolulu, J-DET at Yokosuka, and the JMSDF's JOED at Yokosuka.[8]

The character and composition of the ocean surveillance information collection networks has also changed materially since the early 1990s. Many of the *Classic Bullseye* HF DF stations in the Pacific were dismantled, though fewer than were dismantled in Europe, reflecting both the disappearance of the threat of the Soviet Pacific fleet and the US Navy's increasing reliance on electronic surveillance satellites to detect, track and identify vessels by intercepting their VHF and UHF emissions. However, the United States continued to maintain two large HF DF CDAAs in Japan. One, with an AN/FLR-9 CDAA, was at Misawa; the United States announced in November 2012 that it would cease operations 'early' in 2013 and would be dismantled sometime later in 2013.[9] The other, code-named Project *Camelus*, is at Camp Hansen in Okinawa, which replaced the controversial AN/FRD-10 CDAA at Hanza, 20 kilometres away, in 2007.[10]

With respect to satellite surveillance, the US Navy maintained for many years a Naval Ocean Surveillance System (NOSS) which consisted of constellations of small satellites deployed in circular low earth orbits (LEOs) with an altitude of about 450 kilometres to detect and record the electronic emissions from vessels at sea, especially Soviet ships and submarines. These satellites were initially called *White Cloud*, *Parcae* and *Advanced Parcae*, with the associated ground stations called *Classic Wizard*. The current generation of US Navy LEO ELINT satellites, the first of which was launched on 8 September 2001, is code-named *Intruder*, with *Ranger* being the unclassified designation. The *Intruder* satellites

6 Friedman, *Naval Institute Guide*, p. 7.
7 'OSIS Ocean Surveillance Information System', *Global Security*, at www.globalsecurity.org/intell/systems/obu.htm
8 ibid; 'CV: Senior Systems Security Engineer', at space-careers.com/agency/cvview_7971.html
9 Armando R. Limon, 'Misawa to Tear Down Massive "Elephant Cage" Antennae', *Stars and Stripes*, 19 November 2012; 'U.S. Military's "Elephant Cage" Antenna to be Razed', *Japan Times*, 22 November 2012, at www.japantimes.co.jp/news/2012/11/22/national/u-s-militarys-elephant-cage-antenna-to-be-razed/#.Uj_kUX-Kq9J
10 Richelson, *US Intelligence Community*, p. 228; 'Construction of New "Elephant Cage" at Camp Hansen, Okinawa', *Asahi Shimbun*, 13 February 2005, at www.asahi.com/politics/update/0213/002.htm

The Tools of Owatatsumi

detect and record land-based radars and other electronic emissions as well as sea-based emissions; the *Advanced Parcae* satellites also had this dual capability, but the detection systems aboard the *Intruders* are evidently considerably more advanced. Since the mid-1980s, there has been increasing participation of Army and Air Force SIGINT personnel in the program.[11] The *Ranger/Intruder* satellites also have a COMINT Mapping capability for systematically mapping the locations of communications transmitters in designated areas around the globe.[12]

The ground segment of the *Intruder* system consists of four ground stations code-named *ICEBox* (with 'ICE' being an acronym for improved collection equipment) that are located at Vandenberg Air Force Base, California; in Germany; at Diego Garcia in the Indian Ocean; and about 16 kilometres north of Misawa.[13] The *ICEBox* station at Misawa was established in 1997. It had two 10.5-metre diameter radomes in September 1998.[14] (For a brief period there was a sign at the entrance to the station which identified the facility as 'NSGA Misawa ICEBox Compound').[15] Foundations for a third radome were completed in December 2004.[16] By around 2006 it had five radomes, four of which were for *ICEBox* data reception and one of which housed a satellite communications dish. These had all been removed by 2007–08. Google Earth imagery dated 12 September 2012 shows, however, that two new *ICEBox* radomes had been restored on the foundations that were built for the third and fourth *ICEBox* radomes. The 2010 edition of the Misawa Air Base Telephone Directory lists *ICEBox* Operations at the *ICEBox* ground station (0176–59–3458) and the *ICEBox* Operations Chief at the Misawa Air Base (226–2607).[17]

In the case of the US Navy's SOSUS systems, most of those in the north Pacific were closed in the early 1990s. Greater reliance was placed on SURTASS vessels, with towed arrays, which can be moved from ocean to ocean according to operational requirements and are even able to support deployed forces in tactical roles. Four SURTASS ships were commissioned in 1991–93 and a fifth,

---

11   Jeffrey T. Richelson, *The US Intelligence Community* (Westview Press, Boulder, Colorado, sixth edition, 2012) pp. 209–11.

12   Michael K. Buckingham, 'Resume', at http://www.mikesbaux.org/resume.doc.

13   'ECHELON Station Griesheim with Darmstadt', at hp.kairaven.de/miniwahr/darmstadt-griesheim.html; Richelson, *The US Intelligence Community*, pp. 215–17; 'K-Engineering Services and Technical Support of the Single Consolidated Baseline (SCB) Equipment Suite', *Federal Business Opportunities*, 29 October 2004, at www.fbo.gov/index?s=opportunity&mode=form&id=34708387d7cfe2178d03f78917479e38&tab=core&_cview=0

14   'The Truth About Misawa: The Ping-pong Balls Which Multiply', 2 May 2000, at www.toonippo.co.jp/rensai/ren2000/misawa/msw0502.html

15   Young Spiegel, 'U.S. Listening Stations at Misawa Designed to Uncover Russian and DPRK Military Secrets', at www.globalview.cn/ReadNews.asp?NewsID=30553

16   Grant Sattler, '"Icebox" Project Receives a "Warm" Navy Welcome', *Pacific Engineer*, April 2005, pp. 16–17, at www.pod.usace.army.mil/News/Pacific_Engineer_1_.pdf

17   '2010 Telephone Directory, Misawa Air Base, Japan', p. 31.

the *Impeccable* (T-AGOS 23), in 1998. In any case, by the end of the Cold War the US Navy had transferred all its SOSUS systems in Japanese waters to the JMSDF, and instituted arrangements for US Navy teams to be stationed at some of the JMSDF facilities and for some of the systems to be managed by a joint US Navy/ JMSDF office at Yokosuka. And as already noted, the US Navy evidently laid a new SOSUS array in 2006 in the area between Kyushu and Okinawa, dividing the East China Sea from the Pacific Ocean, and presumably connected to the JMSDF's Ocean Observation Station at White Beach in Okinawa.[18]

---

18 「ケーブル敷設艦・測量艦の佐世保入港増加の意味は?」['What is the Significance of an Increased Number of Sasebo Port Visits by Cable-laying Ships?'], at www.rimpeace.or.jp/jrp/sasebo/ sasebobase/0608ssbzeusags.html

13. The Maritime Safety Agency (MSA) / Japan Coast Guard (JCG)

The Maritime Safety Agency (MSA), which was officially renamed the Japan Coast Guard (JCG) in April 2000, is effectively a fourth branch of the Japanese military. Originally established as the Maritime Safety Board in April 1948, it has been reorganised many times since then, and its roles and missions have expanded to include not only guarding Japan's enormous coastline and providing search and rescue services, but also constabulary operations in the sea lanes and high seas.[1] In May 1998, two MSA vessels were sent to Singapore ready to evacuate Japanese residents from Indonesia, where the political situation was 'unstable' and 'unpredictable'.[2] Since 1996, the MSA/JCG has been increasingly involved in protecting the Senkaku Islands and policing other disputed areas in the East China Sea.[3] JCG patrol boats sank a suspected North Korean 'spy ship' near Amami–Oshima Island in December 2001.[4] It is the primary Japanese agency in the US-led Proliferation Security Initiative (PSI), which involves the interdiction of ships on the high seas suspected of carrying weapons of mass destruction or related materials.[5] In September 2003 the JSG represented Japan in the PSI exercise in the Coral Sea off the north-east coast of Australia.[6] In January 2008, armed JCG officers accompanied Japanese whaling ships being confronted by protest boats in the Southern Ocean near Antarctica.[7]

Although part of the Ministry of Transportation, in reality the MSA functions as a quasi-autonomous and capable maritime defence force, with its own ships and aircraft. Indeed, the Japanese Maritime Self-Defense Force (JMSDF) grew out of the MSA – for its first four months, from April to August 1952, it was organised as the Maritime Security Force within the MSA.[8] The MSA now has about 500 ships, including 350 patrol vessels and other surveillance vessels, oil boom craft, and aids to navigation tenders; 28 land-based aircraft, including

1   Richard J. Samuels, 'New Fighting Power', pp. 84–112.
2   Maritime Safety Agency (MSA), *Annual Report on Maritime Safety: 1998 Edition* (Tokyo, 1998), pp. 7–8.
3   ibid., pp. 16–17.
4   'N. Korean Spy Ship Shown to Public at Kagoshima Dock', 17 May 2003, at findarticles.com/p/articles/mi_mOXPQ/is_2003_May_20/ai_102043547
5   Samuels, 'New Fighting Power', pp. 108–09.
6   'Address by the Hon Alexander Downer MP, at the Third Australia–Japan Conference Dinner', 11 February 2005, at www.foreignminister.gov.au/speeches/2005/050211_3rd_aust_japan_conf.html
7   'Sea Shepherd Being Pursued by Armed Japanese Coast Guard', *Sea Shepherd News*, 30 January 2008, at www.seashepherd.org/news.media_080130_2.html
8   Auer, *Postwar Rearmament*, chapter 5.

five YS-11As equipped for maritime surveillance and associated tasks; and some three dozen helicopters.[9] It has about 12,250 personnel, or more than a quarter of the manpower of the JMSDF.[10]

The HQ of the JCG is in the main building of the Ministry of Transportation in Kasumigaseki in Tokyo. It has three operational departments: Guard and Rescue, Hydrography and Oceanography, and Maritime Traffic Management (formerly called Aids to Navigation). It is organised into 11 regions, with HQs in Otaru in Hokkaido, Shiogama in Miyagi Prefecture in the north-eastern part of Honshu, Yokohama, Nagoya, Kobe, Hiroshima, Kitakyushu in the north-eastern corner of Kyushu, Maizuru, Niigata, Kagoshima in southern Kyushu, and Naha in Okinawa. It has 66 coast guard offices, 54 coast guard stations, seven traffic advisory service centres, and five district communications centres.[11]

The Hydrography and Oceanography Department, which has 13 survey vessels, publishes nautical charts, issues bulletins on ocean conditions, and maintains the Japan Oceanographic Data Center (JODC).[12] The JODC archives and disseminates oceanographic data obtained from various Japanese marine research institutes.[13] It also maintains four hydrographic observatories, located at Hachijo-jima in the Izu Islands, about 300 kilometres south of Tokyo, which specialise in geomagnetic observations; Shimosato, near the southern tip of the Kii Peninsula in Wakayama Prefecture; Shirahama, on the south-eastern side of the Kii Strait; and at the Bisei Astronomical Observatory in Okayama Prefecture, which produces astronomical almanacs for navigational purposes.[14]

The Guard and Rescue Department has a network of shore-based communications stations throughout Japan which maintain continuous watch on international maritime distress radio frequencies, as part of the Global Maritime Distress and Safety System (GMDSS), as well as an alerting system designed to provide prompt and appropriate search and rescue actions. It also maintains the Japanese Ship Reporting System (JASREP), established in 1985, which receives and processes information about the positions and sailing plans of vessels as provided to them by HF radio to the JCG's communications stations.[15]

9   Sharpe (ed.), *Jane's Fighting Ships, 2000–2001*, pp. 387–96.
10   IISS, *The Military Balance 2007* (London, January 2007), p. 357.
11   Japan Coast Guard (JCG), 'Organization', at www.mlit.go.jp/e/shigoto/soshiki/honcho/index_e.htm
12   JCG, 'Hydrographic and Oceanographic Department', at www1.kaiho.mlit.go.jp/jhd-E.html
13   'Japan Oceanographic Data Center', at www.jodc.go.jp/
14   JCG, 'Geomagnetic Observations at the Hachijo Hydrographic Observatory', at www1.kaiho.mlit.go.jp/ KOHO/report/index_gm.html; JCG, 'Shimosato Hydrographic Observatory', 1 September 2004, at www1. kaiho.mlit.go.jp/KOHO/simosato/English/index.htm; JCG, 'Hydrographic and Oceanographic Department'; 'Organization', at www1.kaiho.mlit.go.jp/INFO/Admin/org2.GIF
15   JCG, 'Guard and Rescue Department: Information Gathering System', 海上法案庁 [Japan Coast Guard], at www.kaiho.mlit.go.jp/e/shigoto/keikyu/kainai05_e.htm

A network of HF DF stations was established in the 1970s to maintain a listening watch on marine distress frequencies and to determine the location of emergency transmissions, as well as to monitor suspicious signals. Most of these stations were closed in 1999, or soon after, when the HF watch ceased as part of the GDMSS, having been superseded by VHF radio (Channel 16 on 156.8 megahertz) and satellite communications systems.[16]

In August 1980, the MSA monitored ship-to-ship radio communications indicating that at least nine crew had died in a fire on an Echo I-class nuclear-powered attack submarine, K-122, following a reactor accident, about 130 kilometres east of Okinawa.[17]

In the 1980s and through the early 1990s, the MSA maintained a 9-element HF DF at Cape Soya, near Wakkanai, for search and rescue purposes. The MSA station at Cape Soya was involved in the aftermath of the shooting down of the KAL 007 jetliner on the morning of 1 September 1983, assisting with the search for debris and monitoring Soviet activities in the search area, although MSA ships and aircraft were initially dispatched to the wrong area.[18]

An 8-element HF DF system was established by the MSA near Shiraho, on Ishigaki Island, at the southern end of the Ryukyu island chain, about 200 kilometres east of Taiwan, in 1978. The antenna system consisted of eight masts, about 16 metres tall, arranged in a 24-metre diameter circle, with a small hut in the centre. It was closed in 1999. (The antenna system was dismantled, but the site was still neatly maintained when it was visited in February 2003. The cement blocks which held the masts and the supporting guy wires were still there, as well as the central hut and the sign relating its 'SOS' abilities.)

The local residents of Ishigaki-jima were never impressed with the abilities of the MSA station. They tell a story about the failure of the station, soon after it was built, to detect the distress calls of a sailor in trouble. The failure was especially significant to the Ishigaki residents, many of whom are engaged in fishing and are dependent on safe navigation and reliable search and rescue services. It is said that the station 'malfunctioned'; whatever the cause, it did not detect the signal transmitted on the emergency frequency. The sailor was saved because an amateur ('ham') radio operator picked up his signal.

In 2007–08, the JCG established a 7-element circularly disposed antenna array (CDAA) near the town of Tozato, in the south-eastern part of the island. (Google Earth satellite imagery dated 1 July 2007 shows a normal agricultural field, but

16 US Coast Guard Navigation Center, 'GMDSS Systems', at www.navcen.uscg.gov/marcomms/Gmdss/gmdss_systems.htm
17 *Times* (London), 7 October 1986.
18 R.W. Johnson, *Shoot-down: Flight 007 and the American Connection* (Viking, New York, 1986), pp. 192–93.

TerraServer imagery dated 16 March 2008 shows the complete antenna array and associated small buildings). The site is on flat land about 60 metres above sea level, on the western side of Route 390. It is located between the small villages of Oozato, about 1 kilometre south, and Minami Hoshino, less than 1 kilometre north. The Sokohara Dam is about 2 kilometres to the west, while the coast is about 500 metres to the east. The array is slightly larger than the Japanese Ground Self-defence Force's new 7-element systems installed at Wakkanai, Nemuro, Kobunato and Tachiarai in 2007–10. The circular ground mat is about 120 metres in diameter, and the distance between each of the seven antennas is about 43 metres (see Plates 23 and 24). It is undoubtedly principally concerned with interception and direction-finding (DF) of maritime radio traffic around the Senkaku Islands and other areas in the East China Sea.

14. Assessment of Japan's Ocean Surveillance Capabilities

The underwater approaches to Japan are now guarded by the most advanced submarine detection system in the world. Some 30 hydrophone arrays form a multi-layered network, with the ocean observation stations at Higashidori in north-eastern Honshu and at White Beach in Okinawa operating long-range, open-ocean systems for surveillance of the eastern and southern approaches to the home islands, and another long-range system deployed across the Sea of Japan for surveillance of the western side; the 'barrier' systems, covering the northern and southern entrances to the Sea of Japan (i.e., the Soya and Tsushima straits), and both sides of the Tsugaru Strait separating Hokkaido and Honshu, as well as Kii Strait, the southern entrance to Osaka Bay and the Inland Sea; and short-range systems guarding important harbours and entranceways, as at Kannon Zaki in the case of the entrance to Tokyo Bay and Mutsure-jima at the western entrance to Kanmon Strait and the Inland Sea. Technically, the hydrophones are perhaps the most sophisticated in the world, being as good as the latest US systems.

Beyond securing the underwater approaches to Japan itself, Japan and the United States have over the past decade jointly constructed a long line of undersea surveillance systems (the 'Fish Hook Undersea Defense Line') which extends from the Tsushima Strait and Kyushu along the Ryukyu archipelago, past Taiwan and into maritime South-East Asia. This ensures that Chinese submarines are unable to proceed undetected from either the East China Sea or the South China Sea into the broad expanses of the Pacific Ocean. It suggests that even without recourse to the overwhelming US assets, Japan would be ascendant in any postulated submarine engagement with China.

This notional superiority is extremely tenuous, however, being essentially dependent on Chinese forbearance. Some of the elements of the surveillance infrastructure, including the electronic intelligence (ELINT)/electronic support measures (ESM) facilities and the communications links between the collection stations and the intelligence analysis centres and fleet commands are susceptible to electronic jamming. All of the shore stations for the undersea arrays and the associated ELINT systems are physically vulnerable. Most could easily be destroyed by commando units or precision-guided conventional munitions, let alone the blast overpressures of nuclear detonations. This vulnerability feeds escalation dynamics, with reciprocal pressures to escalate once conflict is joined – pressures on Japan to destroy or damage as much of the Chinese naval forces as possible in the theatre (including Chinese submarines) before its ability to locate and track them is lost, and pressures on the Chinese forces to destroy Japan's sound surveillance system (SOSUS) shore stations and ELINT/ESM facilities before they are decimated.

Some facilities, such as the JMSDF's Ocean Observation Station at White Beach, Okinawa, might be regarded as sufficiently important as to warrant pre-emptive nuclear attack. It is the key station for processing and analysing data collected by the underwater arrays strung from along the Ryukyu archipelago, and hence for detecting submarine movements within and from the East China Sea.

The United States cannot avoid entanglement in this escalation process. Apart from its obligations under the Japan–US Treaty of Mutual Cooperation and Security, important elements of the US Ocean Surveillance Information System (OSIS) are co-located with their JMSDF counterparts. The segment of the 'Fish Hook' line from Kyushu to Yonaguni is essentially a joint activity that is just as vital to US strategic interests as to the defence of Japan. The US Navy could not abide its degradation. At a minimum, it would be compelled to attempt to destroy any Chinese missile-carrying submarines while aware of their locations, before they are able to pass through a broken 'Fish Hook' line and come within firing range of the continental United States. Moreover, the United States has incorporated options in its nuclear war plans to initiate 'selective' and 'limited' nuclear attacks against Chinese targets in a wide range of contingencies, including a conventional conflict between Japan and China as well as situations where its own strategic interests are threatened. The escalatory portents are horrendous.[1]

---

1   For a more comprehensive discussion of the escalation dynamics that might operate in a Northeast Asian conflict, see Robert Ayson & Desmond Ball, 'Can a Sino–Japanese War Be Controlled?', *Survival* (Vol. 56, No. 6), December 2014/January 2015, pp. 135–166.

Bibliography

Japanese Government sources

Diet

第０６７回国会、沖縄及び北方問題に関する特別委員会、第１号、昭和四十六年十二月二十八日 [67th Diet, Special Committee on Okinawa and the Northern Problem, 18 December 1971], at kokkai.ndl.go.jp/SENTAKU/sangiin/067/1650/06712281650001c.html

Ministry of Defense/Self-Defense Forces (SDF)

「洋業務群司令、横須賀」　海上自衛隊 ['Oceanographic Command, Yokosuka', MSDF] at www.soumu.go.jp/kanku/kanto/kanagawa/pdf/kanagawa18_01_07.pdf

「仮屋磁気測定所, 阪神基地隊について」 ['Kariya Magnetic Measurement Station, Hanshin Base Group'], JMSDF, at www.mod.go.jp/msdf/hanshin/about/kariya/index.html

「 紀伊警備所」、JMSDF阪神基地 ['Kii Guard Station', JMSDF Hanshin Base], at www.mod.go.jp/msdf/hanshin/about/kii/index.html

「六連警備所」海上自衛隊 ['Mutsure Coastal Defense Station', MSDF], at www.dii.jda.go.jp/msdf/mf/rekishi/rekishi-1.htm

「我が国の防衛と予算, 平成２５年度概算要求の概要」 [Defense Programs and Budget of Japan, Overview of FY 2013 Budget Request], 防衛省 [Ministry of Defense], September 2012, at www.mod.go.jp/j/yosan/2013/gaisan.pdf

SDF contracts

「平成18年度　9月期　随意契約一覧表」海上自衛隊艦船補給処管理部長, 市川 順, 神奈川県横須賀市田浦港町無番地。['List of Negotiated Contracts for Period 24 September 2006', General Manager, MSDF Ship depot, Tauriminato, Yokosuka, Kanagawa Prefecture), at www.mod.go.jp/msdf/bukei/yd/nyuusatsu/200609.pdf

「海幕公示第３号、１９．１０．１２、一部訂正１９．１０．２３. 自衛艦のとう載武器等の検査・修理工事の契約希望者募集要項」、防衛書 ['Sea Acts, Public Notice No. 3, 12 October 2007, with Corrections 23

October 2007. Guidelines for Applicants for Construction Contracts, such as Inspection and Repair of MSDF Ship-mounted Weapons', Ministry of Defense], at www.mod.go.jp/msdf/bukei/m0/nyuusatsu/K-19-2020-0003.pdf

「艦船の検査・修理等工事の契約希望者募集要項」，海幕公示第、　海幕公示第３号２０．１０．８、防衛省 ['Guidelines for Applicants for Construction Contracts, such as Inspection and Repair of Vessels', Sea Acts, Public Notice No. 3, 8 October 2008. Ministry of Defense], at www.mod.go.jp/msdf/bukei/t1/nyuusatsu/K-20-0000-0003.pdf

「艦船の検査・修理等工事の契約希望者募集要項」，海幕公示第、　海幕公示第３号２１．１０．７、防衛省 ['Guidelines for Applicants for Construction Contracts, such as Inspection and Repair of Vessels', Sea Acts, Public Notice No. 3, 7 October 2009. Ministry of Defense], at www.mod.go.jp/msdf/bukei/d0/nyuusatsu/K-21-2610-0043.pdf

Other national government ministries and agencies

国土地理院 [National Geographical Survey Institute], at watchizu.gsi.go.jp/watchizu.aspx?id=65453150&slidex=0&slidey=800

「警戒監視情報の収集態勢（１）：陸上及び海上自衛隊」，　アジア太平洋地域の安全保障環境と地域的な安全保障のための取組，　第５回「安全保障と防衛力に関する懇談会」資料，　平成１６年６月２９日 ['Maritime Surveillance and Intelligence Collection (1) JGSDF and JMSDF'], *Asia-Pacific Security Environment and Measures for Regional Security*, Council on Security and Defense Capabilities, 29 June 2004, at www.kantei.go.jp/jp/singi/ampobouei/dai5/5siryou.pdf

Prefectural government

『沖縄県の基地の現状』、沖縄県、　沖縄県総務部知事公室，平成15年３月 ['State of the Bases in Okinawa Prefecture', Public Affairs Office, Governor of Okinawa Prefecture, March 2003], at www.pref.okinawa.jp/kititaisaku/D-mokuji.htm

Japanese non-government sources

「旭川飛行場」　['JGSDF Asahikawa Base'], Wikipedia – Japanese, at ja.wikipedia.org/wiki/%E6%97%AD%E5%B7%9D%E9%A3%9B%E8%A1%8C%E5%A0%B4

「壱岐警備所」長崎平和会 ['Iki Guard Station', Nagasaki Peace Committee], at www7b.biglobe.ne.jp/~chi-tan/iki.html

「出雲駐屯地」 ['Izumo Garrison'], Wikipedia – Japanese, at ja.wikipedia.org/wiki/%E5%87%BA%E9%9B%B2%E9%A7%90%E5%B1%AF%E5%9C%B0

「今津駐屯地」 ['Imazu Garrison'], Wikipedia – Japanese, at ja.wikipedia.org/wiki/%E4%BB%8A%E6%B4%A5%E9%A7%90%E5%B1%AF%E5%9C%B0

「ＬＦＡソナー搭載艦２隻、那覇軍港に同時寄港」['Two LFA Sonar-equipped Ships in Simultaneous Call at Naha Naval Base'], Rimpeace, at www.rimpeace.or.jp/jrp/okinawa/080123lfalfa.html

「沿岸監視隊_(陸上自衛隊)」 ['Coastal Monitoring Teams (GSDF)'], Wikipedia – Japanese, at ja.wikipedia.org/wiki/%E6%B2%BF%E5%B2%B8%E7%9B%A3%E8%A6%96%E9%9A%8A_(%E9%99%B8%E4%B8%8A%E8%87%AA%E8%A1%9B%E9%9A%8A)

「呉地方隊」, ['Kure District Command'], Wikipedia – Japanese, at ja.wikipedia.org/wiki/%E5%91%89%E5%9C%B0%E6%96%B9%E9%9A%8A

「舞鶴地方隊」 ['Maizuru District Command'], Wikipedia – Japanese, at ja.wikipedia.org/wiki/%E8%88%9E%E9%B6%B4%E5%9C%B0%E6%96%B9%E9%9A%8A

「大湊地方隊」 ['Ominato District Command'], Wikipedia – Japanese, at ja.wikipedia.org/wiki/%E5%A4%A7%E6%B9%8A%E5%9C%B0%E6%96%B9%E9%9A%8A

「沖縄海洋観測所」、地球探検の旅['Okinawa Ocean Observatory', Journey to Explore the Earth], 19 February 2008, at earthjp.net/mercury/0802190004.html

「沖縄基地」 ['Okinawa Bases'], Wikipedia – Japanese, at ja.wikipedia.org/wiki/%E6%B2%96%E7%B8%84%E5%9F%BA%E5%9C%B0

「佐世保地方隊」 ['Sasebo District Command'], Wikipedia – Japanese, at ja.wikipedia.org/wiki/%E4%BD%90%E4%B8%96%E4%BF%9D%E5%9C%B0%E6%96%B9%E9%9A%8A

'中国艦隊通過　外洋進出に懸念　政府「動き注視」' ['Government Concerned to "Watch Movements" of Chinese Fleet Transiting to the Open Ocean'], *Japan Research Center of Military Affairs*, 14 April 2010, at www.kamiura.com/whatsnew/continues_398.html

「音響測定艦、駆逐艦、揚陸艦がＷＢに同時入港」['Acoustic Measurement Ship, Destroyer, Landing Ship Simultaneously Enter Port at White Beach'], Rimpeace, 13 April 2008, at www.rimpeace.or.jp/jrp/okinawa/080413wb.html

「音響測定艦がもう一隻いた － ビクトリアス、ホワイトビーチに寄港」['One Acoustic Measurement Ship, and then Another – Victorious Enters White Beach'], Rimpeace, 18 January 2008, at www.rimpeace.or.jp/jrp/okinawa/041124wb.html

「音響測定艦ロイヤル、ホワイトビーチに寄港」['Acoustic Measurement Ship Royal Enters White Beach'], Rimpeace, 18 January 2008, at www.rimpeace.or.jp/jrp/okinawa/070815loyal.htm

「音響測定艦、那覇軍港に交代寄港」['Acoustic Measurement Ships Alternate Calls at Naha Port'], Rimpeace, 22 July 2007, at www.rimpeace.or.jp/jrp/okinawa/0712tagosnaha.html

「音響測定艦エフェクティブ、那覇、ＷＢに連続寄港」['Acoustic Measurement Ship in Continuous Port Calls at Naha and White Bay'], Rimpeace, 13 April 2008, at www.rimpeace.or.jp/jrp/okinawa/080407tagos21.html

「音響測定艦エフェクティブ、ＷＢに短時間寄港」['Acoustic Measurement Ship "Effective" Calls Briefly at White Beach'], Rimpeace, at www.rimpeace.or.jp/jrp/okinawa/080314effective.html

「音響測定艦の主な活動海域」['Areas of Acoustic Measurement Ship's Main Activities'], Rimpeace, 21 December 2007, at www.rimpeace.or.jp/jrp/umi/northd/lfaoperation.htm

「海上自衛隊　飯岡受信所」，アンテナの見える風景 ['JMSDF Iioka Receiving Station', *Landscapes with a View of the Antennas*], at home.p04.itscom.net/yama/Iioka/Iioka.htm

「海上自衛隊市原送信所」，アンテナの見える風景 ['JMSDF Ichihara Transmitting Station', *Landscapes with a View of the Antennas*], at home.p04.itscom.net/yama/Ichihara/Icihara.htm

「海上自衛隊　上野原送信所」,アンテナの見える風景 ['JMSDF Uenohara Transmitting Station', *Landscapes with a View of the Antennas*], at home.p04.itscom.net/yama/Uenohara/Uenohara.htm

「海上自衛隊　串良送信所, 'JMSDF Kushira Transmitting Station', September 2009, at home.p04.itscom.net/yama/Kushira/Kushira.htm

「海上自衛隊　館山航空基地」, アンテナの見える風景 ['JMSDF Tateyama Transmitting Station', *Landscapes with a View of the Antennas*], at home.p04. itscom.net/yama/Tateyama_kichi/Tateyama.htm

「海上自衛隊　千代ヶ崎送信所」,　アンテナの見える風景　 ['JMSDF Chiyogasaki Transmitting Station', *Landscapes with a View of the Antennas*], at home.p04.itscom.net/yama/Chiyogasaki/Chiyogasaki.htm

「海上自衛隊　根占受信所」,　アンテナの見える風景 ['JMSDF Nejime Receiving Station', *Landscapes with a View of the Antennas*], September 2009, at home.p04.itscom.net/yama/Nejime/Nejime.htm

「海上自衛隊　横須賀基地　システム通信隊 (受信所・通信所))、ア ンテナの見える風景 ['JMSDF Yokosuka Base, System Communications Unit', *Landscapes with a View of the Antennas*], at home.p04.itscom.net/ Yokosuka_kichi/Yokosuka_kichi.htm

「横須賀地方隊」, ['Yokosuka District Command'], Wikipedia – Japanese, at ja.wikipedia.org/wiki/%E6%A8%AA%E9%A0%88%E8%B3%80%E5% 9C%B0%E6%96%B9%E9%9A%8A

「海洋観測艦「にちなん」の活動について　17．1．21　(海上自衛隊海 上幕僚監部)」, 徒然日記「多事某論」保管庫, ['Activities of the Ocean Surveillance Ship "Nichinan", 21 January 2005 (JMSDF Maritime Staff Office)', At a Loose End Diary: "A Certain Theory about Many Events"], 25 January 2005, at bosc1945.exblog.jp/1844865

「上対馬警備所」、長崎平和委員会 ['Kamitsushima Guard Station', Nagasaki Peace Committee], at www7b.biglobe.ne.jp/~chi-tan/kamitsushima.html

株式会社ゼニライトブイ, 「会社の出来事、平成3年度 1993」 [Zeni Lite Buoy Company, 'Company Events, Fiscal Year 1993'], at www.zenilite.co.jp/ topics/p14.html

「ケーブル敷設艦・ 測量艦の佐世保入港増加の意味は?」['What is the Significance of an Increased Number of Sasebo Port Visits by Cable-laying Ships?'], Rimpeace, 1 September 2006, at www.rimpeace.or.jp/jrp/sasebo/ sasebobase/0608ssbzeusags.html

「県内自衛隊施設数は１６９,件数は減少したが機能は強化」['SDF Facilities in the Prefecture Decline to 169, but Their Functions are Enhanced', *Nagasaki Peace Committee News*], 2 October 2002, at www7b.biglobe. ne.jp/~chi-tan/news/news021019.html

「県内自衛隊施設数量の詳細」、長崎平和委員会 ['Details of SDF Facilities in the Nagasaki Prefecture'], *Nagasaki Peace Committee News*, 31 March 2001, at www7b.biglobe.ne.jp/~chi-tan/nsdf002.html

「県内自衛隊施設数量の詳細」、長崎平和委員会 ['Details of SDF Facilities in Nagasaki Prefecture'], 31 March 2003, at www1.linkclub.or.jp/~chi-tan/nsdf022.html

「郷崎沿岸監視訓練場」、『所管換協議書』ながさき平和委員会、情報開示請求文書第49号 ['Jurisdiction Conversion Consultation Document'], Nagasaki Peace Committee, Information Disclosure Request Document No. 49, at www7b.biglobe.ne.jp/~chi-tan/gozaki.html

「ごらんあれが竜飛岬」 ['Look, there is Tappizaki'], 'Out Camping with my Dog', at www11.plala.or.jp/kei-home/nikki-13-tappi-1.htm

「標津分屯地」 ['Shibetsu Base'], Wikipedia – Japanese, at ja.wikipedia.org/wiki/%E6%A8%99%E6%B4%A5%E5%88%86%E5%B1%AF%E5%9C%B0

「下北海洋観測所」 ['Shimokita Ocean Observation Station'], Wikipedia – Japanese, at ja.wikipedia.org/wiki/%E4%B8%8B%E5%8C%97%E6%B5%B7%E6%B4%8B%E8%A6%B3%E6%B8%AC%E6%89%80

「下対馬警備所」、長崎平和委員会 ['Shimotsushima Guard Station', Nagasaki Peace Committee], at www7b.biglobe.ne.jp/~chi-tan/shimotsushima.html

「下関基地」 ['Shimonoseki Base'], Wikipedia – Japanese, at ja.wikipedia.org/wiki/%E4%B8%8B%E9%96%A2%E5%9F%BA%E5%9C%B0

「白神岬砲台」 ['Shirakami-misaki Battery'], at www006.upp.so-net.ne.jp/fortress/tsugaru/shirakami.htm

「12式地対艦誘導弾」 ['Type-12 Surface-to-Ship Missile'], Wikipedia – Japanese, at ja.wikipedia.org/wiki/12%E5%BC%8F%E5%9C%B0%E5%AF%BE%E8%89%A6%E8%AA%98%E5%B0%8E%E5%BC%BE

『新南極観測船「しらせ」』、日本マリンエンジニアリング学会誌 第45巻 第2号、2010 ['New Antarctic Research Ship', *Journal of the Japan Institute of Marine Engineering*, (Vol. 45, No. 2), 2010], pp. 32–37, at https://www.jstage.jst.go.jp/article/jime/45/2/45_180/_pdf

「宣戦布告」（上）、麻生幾 (著者), 講談社、1998年 [Iku Aso, Sensen Fukoku, (Kodansha, Tokyo, 1988), Vol. 1].

「第301沿岸監視隊」 ['301 Coastal Surveillance Unit'], Wikipedia – Japanese, at ja.wikipedia.org/wiki/%E7%AC%AC301%E6%B2%BF%E5%B2%B8%E7%9B%A3%E8%A6%96%E9%9A%8A

「立神地区自衛隊　佐世保市立神町」, 長崎平和委員会 [MSDF Tategami District, Nagasaki Peace Committee], at www7b.biglobe.ne.jp/~chi-tan/tategamisdf.html

「俵ケ浦半島　向後崎灯台と船番所」, つぐみの笑顔 ['Tawaragauru Peninsula, Ship Guard Station and Kogozaki Lighthouse', Smile of the Thrush], 16 March 2012, at blogs.yahoo.co.jp/yamamuraren/archive/2012/03/16

「向後崎警備所」長崎平和会 ['Kogozaki Guard Station', Nagaski Peace Committee], at www7b.biglobe.ne.jp/~chi-tan/kogozaki.html

「対馬防備隊」 ['Tsushima Defense Group Headquarters'], Wikipedia – Japanese, at ja.wikipedia.org/wiki/%E5%AF%BE%E9%A6%AC%E9%98%B2%E5%82%99%E9%9A%8A

「崎辺地区海上自衛隊　佐世保市崎辺町」, 長崎平和委員会 [MSDF Sakibe District, Nagasaki Peace Committee], at www7b.biglobe.ne.jp/~chi-tan/sakibesdf.html

「名寄駐屯地」 ['JSDF Nayoro Camp'], Wikipedia – Japanese, at ja.wikipedia.org/wiki/%E5%90%8D%E5%AF%84%E9%A7%90%E5%B1%AF%E5%9C%B0

「日本の端（岬／灯台）- 8」、『のんびりし』 ['The Edge of Japan (Capes and Lighthouses)', Part 8, 'Laid Back'], at charider.cside2.com/Nonbiri/nihon/edge8.html

「北方最前線！！　謎のレーダーサイト！？」、千島の桜 – Nakashibetsu Hokkaido ['Northern Frontline, Sakura of Chishima – Nakashibestu Hokkaido], 3 October 2009, at blogs.yahoo.co.jp/panzer_tiger222/archive/2009/10/3

『北海度のC3I基地に見る新たな福強と変化』、松井愈（著者）、1993年日本平和会国際会議、C3I分科会・18th　全道基地闘争活動者会議（93・10）[Matsui Masaru, 'Looking at New Developments and Changes in Hokkaido C³I Bases, Japan Peace Committee International Conference, C3I Sub-committee; and 18th National Base Struggle Activists Conference (October 1993)', Hokkaido Peace Committee Study Document No. 26, 8–1994].

「北海道地方」、『自衛隊イベント情報 [2003年版]』['Hokkaido: Information on JSDF Events 2003'], at www003.upp.so-net.ne.jp/rightwing/event/2003/hokkaido2003.html

「六連島探検 ― 自衛隊元レーダー基地編」、彦中三八ブログ ['Exploring Mitsurejima : Former SDF Radar Station', Hikochu 38 Blog], 4 August 2010, at blog.goo.ne.jp/hikochu38sotu/e/fe817565af03a92589fc4a77ddf1c6a6

「陸自郷崎訓練場が拡張へ」、長崎平和委員会 ['GSDF Gozaki Training Station is to Expand', *Nagasaki Peace Committee News*], 21 February 2002, at www7b.biglobe.ne.jp/~chi-tan/news/news020221.html

「陸自配備 年１２００～１４００万円で与那国と用地賃貸借」、MSN 産経ニュース ['GSDF Deployment: 12–14 *Million Yen Yonaguni Site Annual Lease*'], *MSN-Sankei News*, 19 June 2013, at sankei.jp.msn.com/politics/news/130619/plc13061900380000-n1.htm

「陸上自衛隊 今津駐屯地創立５６周年記念行事(今津駐屯地祭２００８)」,北大路機関 ['56th Anniversary of JGSDF Imazu Detachment', Kitaoji Agency], 24 September 2008, at harunakurama.blog.ocn.ne.jp/kitaooji/2008/09/post_919e.html

「礼文分屯地」 ['Rebun Island Base'], Wikipedia – Japanese, at ja.wikipedia.org/wiki/%E7%A4%BC%E6%96%87%E5%88%86%E5%B1%AF%E5%9C%B0

'JMSDF 監視所 Part 1 – Abandoned Buildings to Monitor the Intruder', 29 November 2009; 'JMSDF 監視所 Part 2 – Ruins of Black and White Photos', 29 November 2009; and 'JMSDF 監視所 Part 3 – Maritime Self-Defense Monitoring Station was Abandoned', 6 December 2009, *Forbidden Kyushu*, at forbiddenkyushu.wordpress.com/category/%E5%BB%83%E5%A2%9F/jmsdf%E7%9B%A3%E8%A6%96%E6%89%80/

'JMSDF Ships – ARC 481 Tsugaru Class', けいのがらくた置き場 [Kei's Boneyard]), at www2c.airnet.ne.jp/junkyard/jmsdf/ARC481Tsugara.html

Japanese Government sources (English)

67th Diet, Special Committee on Okinawa and the Northern Problem, 18 December 1971, at kokkai.ndl.go.jp/SENTAKU/sangiin/067/1650/06712281650001c.html

Department of Guided Weapon Systems, Technical Research and Development Institute (TRDI), at www.mod.go.jp/trdi/en/programs/gm/gm.html

Japan Coast Guard (JCG), 'Geomagnetic Observations at the Hachijo Hydrographic Observatory', at www1.kaiho.mlit.go.jp/KOHO/report/index_gm.html

———, 'Guard and Rescue Department: Information Gathering System', 海上法案庁 [Japan Coast Guard], at www.kaiho.mlit.go.jp/e/shigoto/keikyu/kainai05_e.htm

———, 'Hydrographic and Oceanographic Department', at www1.kaiho.mlit.go.jp/jhd-E.html

———, 'Organization', at www.mlit.go.jp/e/shigoto/soshiki/honcho/index_e.htm

———, 'Shimosato Hydrographic Observatory', 1 September 2004, at www1.kaiho.mlit.go.jp/KOHO/simosato/English/index.htm

Japan Defense Agency (JDA), *Defense of Japan 1987* (The Japan Times, Tokyo, 1987).

———, *Defense of Japan 1988* (The Japan Times, Tokyo, 1988).

———, *Defense of Japan 1991* (The Japan Times, Tokyo, 1991).

———, *Defense of Japan 1993* (The Japan Times, Tokyo, 1993).

'Japan Oceanographic Data Center', at www.jodc.go.jp/

JMSDF, '"Nichinan" Carrying Out Continental Shelf Survey', 10 February 2006, at jmsdf.sakura.ne.jp/news/c-news/18/021002.htm

———, 'Precautionary Surveillance', at www.mod.go.jp/msdf/formal/english/surveillance/

———, '"Shirase" AGB 5002', at www.mod.go.jp/msdf/formal/gallery/ships/agb/index.html

Maritime Safety Agency (MSA), Annual Report on Maritime Safety: 1998 Edition (Tokyo, 1998).

Ministry of Defense, *Defense of Japan 2006* (Tokyo, 2006).

———, 'Mid-Term Defense Program (FY2011–FY2015)', 17 December 2010.

'Press Conference by the Defense Minister', Tokyo, 23 August 2011, at www.mod.go.jp/e/pressconf/2011/08/110823.html

'Press Conference by the Defense Minister Onodera', Ministry of Defense, 31 January 2014, at www.mod.go.jp/e/pressconf/2014/01/140131.html

'Technical Research and Development Institute: Research Centers Addresses', at www.mod.go.jp/trdi/en/misc/address.html

「掃海部隊の歴史」、掃海隊群、海上自衛隊 ['History of Mine-Sweeper Units', Mine-Sweeper Group, JMSDF], at www.mod.go.jp/msdf/mf/history/index.html

'TRDI: Shimokita Test Center', at www.mod.go.jp/trdi/en/research/simokita_test_en.html

US Government sources

'2010 Telephone Directory, Misawa Air Base, Japan'.

Dawn M. Maskell, 'The Navy's Best-Kept Secret: Is IUSS Becoming a Lost Art?' (Master's thesis, Marine Corps Command and Staff College, Quantico, Virginia, April 2001), at www.dtic.mil/cgi-bin/GetTRDoc?AD=ADA401150

Foreign Affairs and National Defense Division, Congressional Research Service, *Evaluation of Fiscal Year 1979 Arms Control Impact Statements: Toward More Informed Congressional Participation in National Security Policymaking* (US Government Printing Office, Washington, DC, 3 January 1978).

'K-Engineering Services and Technical Support of the Single Consolidated Baseline (SCB) Equipment Suite', *Federal Business Opportunities*, 29 October 2004, at https://www.fbo.gov/index?s=opportunity&mode=form&id=3470 8387d7cfe2178d03f78917479e38&tab=core&_cview=0

Memorandum from the Chief of Naval Operations, 'Disestablishment of Navy Information Operations Command, Misawa, Japan and Realignment of Navy Information Operations Command Detachment, Seoul, Korea' (OPNAV Notice 5400, 5 September 2014).

'United States Navy Information Operations Command Misawa: Command History', at www.niocmisawa.navy.mil/history.html

US Coast Guard Navigation Center, 'GMDSS Systems', at www.navcen.uscg.gov/marcomms/Gmdss/gmdss_systems.htm

US Congress, Office of Technology Assessment (OTA), *Holding the Edge: Maintaining the Defense Technology Base, Volume 2 – Appendices* (OTA-ISC-432, January 1990), Appendix H, 'Strategic Technology Management in Japan: Commercial-Military Comparisons', p. 180.

US Department of Defense, 'Contracts for Thursday, February 12, 1998', at www.defenselink.mil/contracts/contract.aspx?contractid=1215

US Naval Technical Mission to Japan, 'Intelligence Targets Japan: Japanese Anti-Submarine Warfare', 8 February 1946, at www.fischer-tropsch.org/primary_documents/gvt_reports/USNAVY/USNTMJ%20Reports/USNTMJ-200I-0244-0309%20Report%20S-24.pdf

——, 'Intelligence Targets Japan: Defenses of Tsushima and Entrance to Sea of Japan', 11 January 1946, at www.fischer-tropsch.org/primary_documents/gvt_reports/USNAVY/USNTMJ%20Reports/USNTMJ_toc.htm

——, 'Intelligence Targets Japan: Japanese Sonar and Asdic', 14 December 1945, at www.fischer-tropsch.org/primary_documents/gvt_reports/USNAVY/USNTMJ%20Reports/USNTMJ_toc.htm

——, 'Intelligence Targets Japan: Japanese Electronic Harbor Protection Equipment', 14 February 1946, at www.fischer-tropsch.org/primary_documents/gvt_reports/USNAVY/USNTMJ%20Reports/USNTMJ_toc.htm

——, 'Intelligence Targets Japan: Japanese Electronics — General', 29 December 1945, at www.fischer-tropsch.org/primary_documents/gvt_reports/USNAVY/USNTMJ%20Reports/USNTMJ_toc.htm

Books and monographs

Auer, James E., *The Postwar Rearmament of Japanese Maritime Forces, 1945–71* (Praeger, New York, 1973).

Burns, Thomas S., *The Secret War for the Ocean Depths: Soviet-American Rivalry for Mastery of the High Seas* (Rawson Associates, New York, 1978).

Burrows, William E., *Deep Black: Space Espionage and National Security* (Random House, New York, 1986).

Corbett, Julian S. & Edmond J.W. Slade, *Maritime Operations in the Russo-Japanese War* (Admiralty War Staff, London 1914, reprinted by Naval Institute Press, Annapolis, Maryland, 1994), Vol. 2.

Deacon, Richard, *A History of the Japanese Secret Service* (Frederick Muller, London, 1982).

Dibblin, Jane, *Day of Two Suns: U.S. Nuclear Testing and the Pacific Islanders* (New Amsterdam Books, New York, 1990).

Evans, David C. & Mark R. Peattie, *Kaigun: Strategy, Tactics and Technology in the Imperial Japanese Navy, 1887–1941* (Naval Institute Press, Annapolis, Maryland, 1977).

Friedman, Norman, *The Naval Institute Guide to World Naval Weapons Systems, 1997–1998* (Naval Institute Press, Annapolis, Maryland, 1997).

——, *U.S. Submarines Through 1945: An Illustrated Design History* (Naval Institute Press, Annapolis, Maryland, 1995).

Graham, Euan, *Japan's Sea Lane Security, 1940–2004: A Matter of Life and Death?* (Routledge, London, 2006).

Iku Aso, *Sensen Fukoku* (Kodansha, Tokyo, March 1988), Vol. 1.

International Institute for Strategic Studies (IISS), *The Military Balance*, (London), various annual editions.

Jackson, Paul (ed.), *Jane's All the World's Aircraft 1997–98* (Jane's Information Group, Coulsdon, Surrey, 88th edn, 1997).

Johnson, R.W., *Shoot-down: Flight 007 and the American Connection* (Viking, New York, 1986).

Kennedy, Malcolm, *A Short History of Japan* (Mentor, New York, 1964).

Lambert, Mark (ed.), *Jane's All the World's Aircraft 1990–91* (Jane's Information Group, Coulsdon, Surrey, 81st edn, 1990).

Moore, John (ed.), *Jane's Fighting Ships 1982–83* (Jane's Publishing Company, London, 85th edn, 1982).

Morgan, Joseph & Mark Valencia, *Atlas for Marine Policy in East Asian Seas* (University of California, Berkeley, 1992).

National Institute for Defense Studies (NIDS), *East Asian Strategic Review 2001* (Tokyo, 2001).

Operational History of Japanese Naval Communications, December 1941–August 1945 (Aegean Park Press, Laguna Hills, California, 1985).

Parillo, Mark P., *The Japanese Merchant Marine in World War II* (Naval Institute Press, Annapolis, Maryland, 1993).

Person, Bill, *Critic Makers: The Ironworks Incident* (Imprint Books, 2004).

Richelson, Jeffrey T., *Foreign Intelligence Organizations* (Ballinger, Cambridge, Massachusetts, 1988).

——, *The US Intelligence Community* (Westview, Boulder, Colorado, 5th edn, 2008).

Sharpe, Richard (ed.), *Jane's Fighting Ships 1996–97* (Jane's Information Group, Coulsdon, Surrey, 99th edn, 1996).

——(ed.), *Jane's Fighting Ships 2000–2001*, (Jane's Information Group, Coulsdon, Surrey, 103rd edn, 2000).

Storry, Richard, *A History of Modern Japan* (Penguin, Harmondsworth, Middlesex, 1960).

Williamson, John (ed.), *Jane's Military Communications, 1996–97* (Jane's Information Group, Coulsdon, Surrey, 17th edn, 1996).

Woolley, Peter J., *Japan's Navy: Politics and Paradox, 1971–2000* (Lynne Rienner, Boulder, Colorado, 2000).

Articles

Ayson, Robert & Desmond Ball, 'Can a Sino–Japanese War Be Controlled?', *Survival* (Vol. 56, No. 6), December 2014/January 2015.

Ball, Desmond, 'Intelligence Collection Operations and EEZs: The Implications of New Technology', *Marine Policy* (Vol. 28), 2004.

Booda, Larry, 'ASW: A Holding Action? Technical and Political Decisions Intermingle', *Sea Technology*, November 1978.

——, 'Overview of ASW Systems and Their Capabilities', 13 March 1979, transcript.

Browne, Jay R., 'Early Development', *Cryptolog: U.S. Naval Cryptologic Veterans Association* (Vol. 18, No. 4), Fall 1997.

——, 'Kami Seya – The Last Years', *Cryptolog: U.S. Naval Cryptologic Veterans Association* (Vol. 18, No. 4), Fall 1997.

Bussert, James C., 'Oil May be Focal Point of Sino-Japanese Dispute', *Signal*, November 2006, at www.afcea.org/signal/articles/anmviewer.asp?a=1216

——, 'Computers Add New Effectiveness to SOSUS/CAESAR', *Defense Electronics*, October 1979, pp. 59–64.

——, 'Is SOSUS an Underwater Maginot Line?', *Military Electronics/ Countermeasures*, July 1982.

Dutton, Peter A., 'International Law and the November 2004 *Han* Incident', *Asian Security* (Vol. 2, No. 2), 2006, pp. 87–101.

Fanell, James E., 'China: Big Trouble on the High Seas', *Hoover Digest* (No. 3), 2006, at www.hoover.org/publications/digest/4635601.html

Gravely, Samuel L. Jr., 'OSIS Extends Intelligence Coverage Beyond Radar Horizon', *Defense Electronics*, April 1982.

Hancock, Gus, 'OSIS: Forging the Links', *Naval Intelligence Professionals Quarterly*, Summer 1991.

Haruki Kada, Kazuyoshi Mori, Hanako Ogasawara, Toshiaki Nakamura, Takenobu Tsuchiya & Nobuyki Endoh, 'Preliminary Result of Biological Transient Noise Observation Using 2 Sets of 4-Element Hydrophone Array', *Proceedings of Symposium on Ultrasonic Electronics* (Vol. 30), 18–20 November 2009, at www.use-jp.org/USE2010/proceedings/USE09/pdf/1P6-7.pdf

Hideo Sekino, 'Japan and Her Maritime Defense', *US Naval Institute Proceedings* (Vol. 97, No. 819), May 1971.

Hiroshi Asanuma, Mitsuyuki Tanaka, Hiroaki Niitsuma & Ryotaku Sato, 'Development of an Optical Micro Hydrophone for Mass Production', *Society of Exploration Geophysicists*, October 2006, at www.onepetro.org/mslib/servlet/onepetropreview?id=SEG-2006-0436

Hiroshi Kamata, 'Realizing Dreams – Yesterday, Today, Tomorrow – An Acoustic/ Environmental Sensing Technology Based on Optical Fiber Sensors', *Oki Technical Review* (No. 189), April 2002, pp. 43–47, at citeseerx.ist.psu.edu/viewdoc/download?doi=10.1.1.197.1088&rep=rep1&type=pdf

'Japan: State Incapable of Waging War', *Bungei Shinju*, Tokyo, November 1998, pp. 150–57, in FBIS Translated Text, East Asia, FBIS-EAS-98-299, 26 October 1988.

Jyh-Perng Wang & Ing-Chyi Jan, 'On the Event of PRC Han-class Sub Intruding Japan and Conferring the Proper Thoughts of Taiwan Defense', *Taiwan Defense Affairs* (Vol. 5, No. 4), Summer 2005, pp. 72–105.

Kazuyoshi Mori, Hanako Ogasawara & Toshiaki Nakamura, 'Observation Results for Biological Impulsive Noise at Hashirimizu Port in Tokyo Bay', *Memoirs of the National Defense Academy* (Vol. 51, No. 1), May 2011, pp. 1–12.

Kenji Saijyou, Chiaki Okawara, Tomonao Okuyama, Yasuyuki Nakajima & Ryotaku Sato, 'Fiber Bragg Grating Hydrophone with Polarization-maintaining Fiber for Mitigation of Polarization-induced Fading', *Acoustical Science and Technology* (Vol. 33, No. 4), 2012, pp. 239–46.

Liao Wen-chung, 'U.S. Navy's Fish Hook Defence Line Submarine Monitoring Network in the West Pacific', *Defence International*, August 2005, at www.diic.com.tw/mag/mag252/252-74.htm

McCormack, Gavan, 'Yonaguni: Dilemmas of a Frontier Island in the East China Sea', *The Asia-Pacific Journal*, September 2012, at japanfocus.org/-Gavan-McCormack/3837#.

Masao Igarashi & Kazuhiko Nitadori, 'An Advanced SSBL-Acoustic Reference System Using a Planar Hydrophone Array', *Electronics and Communications in Japan (Part 1: Communications)* (Vol. 65, No. 3), 1982, pp. 1–9.

'Militarisering av Haven: USA's Vapen Utvekling Rubbar Grunden for "Terrorbalansen"', *Kommentar*, October 1980.

Motonobu Imasato, Nobuo Kiriya, Hiroshi Asou, Osamu Toyama & Kuniyuki Matsushita, 'Development of Marine Surveillance Technology by Sensing Underwater Sound', *Journal of the Japan Institute of Marine Engineering (JIME)* (Vol. 46, No. 1), 2011, at www.mesj.or.jp/publication/award_paper/ap_papers/pdf/2011AP3.pdf

Naoyuki Agawa & James E. Auer, 'Pacific Friendship', *U.S. Naval Institute Proceedings*, October 1996.

O'Connell, John, 'Strategic Implications of the Japanese SSM-1 Cruise Missile', *Journal of Northeast Asian Studies* (Vol. 6, No. 2), Summer 1987, pp. 53–66.

Parry, Albert & Alexander Kiralfy, 'Soviet Submarines in the Far East', *Public Affairs* (Vol. 10, No. 1), March 1937.

Sagawa Jiro, Kaminuma Katsutada & Ueda Yoshio, 'Sea Gravimeter System of the Icebreaker "SHIRASE"', *Memoirs of National Institute of Polar Research*, September 1984, at ci.nii.ac.jp/naid/110000009895/en/.

Samuels, Richard J., '"New Fighting Power": Japan's Growing Maritime Capabilities and East Asian Security', *International Security* (Vol. 32, No. 3), Winter 2007/08, pp. 84–112.

Sattler, Grant, '"Icebox" Project Receives a "Warm" Navy Welcome', *Pacific Engineer*, April 2005, pp. 16–17, at www.pod.usace.army.mil/News/Pacific_Engineer_1_.pdf

'Sonar – Sub-surface: Caesar', *DMS Market Intelligence Report*, DMS Inc, Greenwich, Connecticut, 1981.

Sourabh Gupta, 'China-Japan Trawler Incident: Reviewing the Dispute Over Senkaku/Daioyu Waters', *East Asia Forum*, 6 December 2010, at www.eastasiaforum.org/2010/12/06/china-japan-trawler-incident-review-of-legalities-understandings-and-practices-in-disputed-senkakudaioyu-waters/

Tetsuo Kawamoto, 'Reorganization of Ground Self-Defense Force Divisions Seen', *Gunji Kenkyu*, May 1987, in Foreign Broadcast Information Service (FBIS), JPRS Report: East Asia, JPRS-JAR-87-005, 2 November 1987, pp. 11–12, at www.dtic.mil/dtic/tr/fulltext/u2/a346884.pdf

Toru Arai, Kazutoshi Ayusawa, Housaki Sato, Tetsuji Miyato, Kazutami Kawamura & Keiichi Kobayashi, 'Properties of Hydrophone with Porous Piezoelectric Ceramics', *Japanese Journal of Applied Physics* (Vol. 30), 1991, pp. 2253–55.

'White Paper: Nuclear War and the Self-Defense Forces', *Sekai*, February 1985, pp. 74–139, in Foreign Broadcast Information Service (FBIS), *Japan Report* (JPRS–JAR–85–013), 9 May 1985, at www.dtic.mil/cgi-bin/GetTRDoc?Location=U2&doc=GetTRDoc.pdf&AD=ADA349828

Wit, Joel S., 'Advances in Antisubmarine Warfare', *Scientific American* (Vol. 244, No. 2), February 1981.

Yukie Yoshikawa, 'Okinotorishima: Just the Tip of the Iceberg', *Harvard Asia Quarterly* (Vol.9, No. 4), 2006, pp. 51–61, at pranj.org/papers/yoshikawa-haq06.htm

——, 'The US-Japan-China Mistrust Spiral and Okinotorishima', *Japan Focus*, 11 October 2007, at www.japanfocus.org/products/details/2541

News reports

'14 Chinese Vessels Spotted Near Senkakus but No Fishing Ship Armada', *Asahi Shimbun*, 19 September 2012, at ajw.asahi.com/article/behind_news/politics/AJ201209190059

'27 "Spy" Ships Operating in Waters Around Japan', *Spy Tech Agency: Intel Bulletin*, 4 January 2002, at www.spytechagency.com/Inte%20Bulletin/Intel%20Bulletin%20020020104.htm

'Another Day, Another 4 Chinese Ships in Japan's Territorial Waters', *Japan Daily Press*, 30 October 2012, at japandailypress.com/another-day-another-4-chinese-ships-in-japans-territorial-waters-3017556/

Baker, Rodger, 'Spy Games: Japan, China Both Newly Ambitious in Asian Waters', *ABC News.Com*, 2 June 2000, at abcnews.go.com/sections/world/DailyNews/stratfor 000602.html

'Beefed-up Okinawa Border Eyed', *Japan Times*, 20 July 2010, at www.japantimes.co.jp/text/nn20100720a5.html

Berkofsky, Alex, 'Tokyo Turns Up the Military Heat', *Asia Times Online*, 16 January 2002, at www.atimes.com/japan-econ/DA16Dh01.html

Buckley, Chris, 'China Cancels Japan Talks, Warns on Sea Dispute', *International Business Times*, 11 September 2010, at m.ibtimes.com/china-japan-sea-61413.html

'China Sails Through "First Island Chain"', *China Daily*, 2 August 2013, at usa.chinadaily.com.cn/china/2013-08/02/content_16863855.htm

'China Says its Naval Vessels' Transit of Osumi Strait Not Threatening', *Mainichi*, 2 May 2012, at mainichi.jp/english/english/newsselect/news/20120502p2g00m0dm019000c.html

'China Threatens Force if Japan Challenges Sovereignty', *RIA Novosti*, 27 October 2012, at en.rian.ru/world/20121027/176955713.html

'China Warns Japan Over Trawler Seizure', *RTT News*, 10 September 2010, at www.rttnews.com/Content/GeneralNews.aspx?Id=1414654&SM=1

'China's Largest Ocean Surveillance Ship and Helicopter Coordinated the First East China Sea Cruise', 15 December 2011, at www.3abc.net/?p=25063

'Chinese Destroyer Sailed Through Tsugaru Strait', *Daily Yomiuri Online*, 22 October 2008, at www.yomiuri.co.jp/dy/national/20081022TDY02307.htm

'Chinese Experts Say the Japanese Military Deployment is Close to Sensitive Areas of China', *China Military Report*, 4 July 2009, at wuxinghongqi.blogspot.com/2009/07/chinese-experts-said-deployment-of.html

'Chinese Government States it Will Continue Patrolling Senkaku Waters', *Japan Daily Press*, 9 October 2012, at japandailypress.com/chinese-government-states-it-will-continue-patrolling-senkaku-waters-0915067/

'Chinese Navy Fleet Enters West Pacific for Routine Training', *Xinhua*, 28 November 2012, at news.xinhuanet.com/english/china/2012-11/28/c_132005111.htm

'Chinese Officials Admit to MSDF Radar Lock Allegations', *Japan Times*, 18 March 2013, at www.japantimes.co.jp/news/2013/03/18/national/chinese-officials-admit-to-msdf-radar-lock-allegations/

'Chinese Patrol Ships Enter Japan Territorial Waters Again', *Asahi Shimbun*, 25 October 2012, at ajw.asahi.com/article/behind_news/politics/AJ201210250060

'Chinese Ships in Territorial Waters Near Senkaku, Once Again', *Japan Daily Press*, 25 October 2012, at japandailypress.com/chinese-ships-in-territorial-waters-near-senkaku-once-again-2517289/

'Chinese Ships Roam Around Okinotori Islands at Will', *Japan Today*, 8 December 2004, at www.japantoday.com/jp/shukan/257

'Chinese Vessel Found to Have Conducted Operations Off Boso Peninsula, Gathering Radio Wave Information During Voyage Around the Japanese Archipelago, Says MSDF', *Sankei*, 10 June 2000, in American Embassy, Tokyo, 'Daily Summary of Japanese Press', 14 June 2000.

Cole, J. Michael, 'PLA Sorties Threaten Encirclement', *Taipei Times*, 9 February 2012, at www.taipeitimes.com/News/front/archives/2012/02/09/2003525025

——, 'In Test, Japan Warship Blasts Missile Launched from Kauai', *Honolulu Advertiser*, 18 December 2007, at the.honoluluadvertiser.com/article/2007/Dec/18/ln/hawaii712180346.html

'Construction of New "Elephant Cage" at Camp Hansen, Okinawa', *Asahi Shimbun*, 13 February 2005, at www.asahi.com/politics/update/0213/002.htm

'Defense Minister Cautious About Deploying GSDF on Westernmost Island', *Kyodo*, 25 September 2009, at www.breitbart.com/article.php?id=D9AU3VE80&show_article=1

'Detailed Report of New Units as at End FY 2007', *Asagumo News*, 3 April 2008, at www.asagumo-news.com/news/200804/080403/08040303.html

'Dynamic Positioning System', 三井造船 [Mitsui Engineering & Shipbuilding] at www.mes.co.jp/english/business/ship/ship_11.html

'Editorial: Japan Responds to China Threat', *Taiwan News.Com*, 11 August 2001, at www.etaiwannews.com/Editorial/2001/08/11/997498010.htm

'Editorial: Why Try to Rock the Boat?', *China Post*, 29 July 2010, at www.chinapost.com.tw/editorial/world-issues/2010/07/29/266563/Why-try.htm

Fackler, Martin, 'Chinese Buoys are Focus of Latest Dispute Over Contested Islands', *New York Times*, 22 February 2013.

——, 'Japan Says China Aimed Military Radar at Ship', *New York Times*, 5 February 2013.

'Foreign Ministry Asks Japan to Release Seized Boat', *China Post*, 17 September 2009, at www.chinapost.com.tw/taiwan/foreign-affairs/2009/09/17/224954/Foreign-ministry.htm

'Foreign Sub Spotted Near Japan's Territorial Waters', *Asahi Shimbun*, 14 May 2013.

'Foreign Submarine Spotted Near Japan's Territorial Waters', *Japan Daily Press*, 14 May 2013, at japandailypress.com/foreign-submarine-spotted-near-japanese-territorial-waters-1428827/

'Gov't Eyes Obtaining Land on Southwestern Isle for Coastal Monitoring', *Mainichi Shimbun*, 21 August 2011.

Hisashi Ishimatsu, 'Far Western Isle a Defence Outpost?', *Asahi Shimbun*, 10 July 2009, at www.asahi.com/english/Herald-asahi/TKY200907100075.html

Huang Jing-jing, 'Chinese Navy Fleet Completes Largest-ever Training in Pacific', *Want China Times*, 25 June 2011, at www.wantchinatimes.com/news-subclass-cnt.aspx?id=20110625000003&cid=1101

'Japan Asks S Korea to End Survey', *BBC News*, 5 July 2006, at news.bbc.co.uk/2/hi/asia-pacific/5149048.stm

'Japan Beefs Up Defense Forces in Yonaguni', *The View from Taiwan*, 6 July 2009, at michaelturton.blogspot.com/2009/07/japan-beefs-up-defense-forces-in.html

'Japan Concerned after Chinese Vessels Seen Again in Osumi Strait', *Want China Times*, 16 June 2012, at www.wantchinatimes.com/news-subclass-cnt.aspx?id=20120616000062&cid=1101

'Japan Discovers Noise Leakage', *Kommersant*, 3 August 2006, at kommersant.com/page.asp?idr=1&id=694770

'Japan Ends Hunt for Submarine Intruder', *Defense News*, 18 September 2009, at www.defensenews.com/story.php?i=3726554

'Japan Installing Missiles on Pacific Gateway Islands', *Taipei Times*, 8 November 2013, at www.taipeitimes.com/News/front/archives/2013/11/08/2003576391

'Japan May Deploy Troops Near Disputed Islands', *China Post*, 3 July 2009, at www.chinapost.com.tw/asia/japan/2009/07/03/214750/Japan-may.htm

'Japan May Place Troops Close to Disputed Islands', *Taipei Times*, 10 November 2010, at www.taipeitimes.com/News/front/archives/2010/11/10/2003488154

'Japan Mulling Over Release of Chinese Radar Data in Senkaku Row', *Japan Daily Press*, 11 February 2013, at japandailypress.com/japan-mulling-over-release-of-chinese-radar-data-in-senkaku-row-1123103

'Japan Mulls Coastal Monitoring Unit in Wake of China's Naval Activity', *Kyodo News*, 21 August 2011, at www.accessmylibrary.com/article-1G1-264916415/japan-mulls-coastal-monitoring.html

'Japan Plans to Name 39 Islets in Disputed, Remote Waters', *Global Times*, 17 January 2012, at www.globaltimes.cn/NEWS/tabid/99/ID/692425/Japan-plans-to-name-39-islets-in-disputed-remote-waters.aspx

'Japan Protests Over China Ships in Disputed Waters', *Reuters*, 24 August 2011, at www.reuters.com/article/2011/08/24/us-japan-china-disputes-idUSTRE77N0R620110824

'Japan Protests to China Over Boats Near Islands', *AFP*, 25 October 2010, at www.aaj.tv/2010/10/japan-protests-to-china-over-boats-near-islands/

'Japan Questions Chinese Buoys Near Senkakus', *Japan Daily Press*, 27 February 2013, at japandailypress.com/japan-questions-chinese-buoys-near-senkakus-2724166/

'Japan Seizes Taiwanese Fishing Boat in Miyakos', *Taipei Times*, 17 November 2008, at www.taipeitimes.com/News/taiwan/archives/2008/11/17/2003428846

'Japan to Deploy Forces Near Tiaoytais', *China Post*, 19 November 2011.

'Japan to Give Up Yonaguni Garrison Only 150 km Away from Diaoyu Islands', *Sankei*, 20 March 2013.

'Japan to Launch Satellites to Monitor Oceans', *Space Daily*, 7 July 2013, at www.spacedaily.com/reports/Japan_to_launch_satellites_to_monitor_oceans_999.html

'Japan to Reassess Plan to Deploy Troops on Yonaguni', *NHK News*, 26 September 2009, at www.nhk.or.jp/news/t10015700241000.html#

'Japan to Send Troops to Remote Isle Over China Fears', *AFP*, 11 November 2010, at www.rsis.edu.sg/research/RMA_bulletin/RMA%20Bulletin%20 2410.pdf

'Japan–U.S. Security Treaty After 50 Years – Phantom Alliance: U.S. Servicemen in the Shadows; Watching Behind Weapons Guidance', *Tokyo Shimbun*, 24 August 2001, in American Embassy, Tokyo, 'Daily Summary of Japanese Press', 28 August 2001.

'Japan Will Buy 10 P1 Planes', *House of Japan*, 18 November 2010, at www. houseofjapan.com/local/japan-will-buy-10-p1-patrol-planes

'Japanese Navy Force Taiwan Boat Back from Disputed Islands', *Asia News*, 14 September 2010, at www.asianews.it/news-en/Japanese-navy-force-Taiwan-boat-back-from-disputed-islands-19453.html

'Japanese Self-Defense Forces Will be Stationed at Diaoyu Islands to Monitor China', 29 June 2013, at www.best-news.us/news-4773774-Japanese-Self-Defense-Forces-will-be-stationed-at-Diaoyu-islands-nearest-to-monitor-China.html

Kallender, Paul, 'Japan–China Island Spat Threatens GSDF Deployment and Much More', *Defense News*, 1 May 2013.

'KHI Gives MSDF First P-1 Anti-Sub Aircraft', *Japan Times*, 27 March 2013.

Kim Soonhi, 'Islanders Split as Ministry Seeks 1.5 Billion Yen to Deploy SDF', *Asahi Shimbun*, 3 October 2011, at ajw.asahi.com/article/behind_news/politics/AJ2011100313047

Kiyoshi Takenaka & Kaori Kaneko, 'Japan Fires Water Cannon to Turn Away Taiwan Boats', *Reuters*, 25 September 2012, at www.reuters.com/article/2012/09/25/us-china-japan-taiwan-idUSBRE88O02C20120925

Lai I-chung, 'Yonaguni Plans Raise Questions of Taiwan', *Taipei Times*, 6 July 2009, at www.taipeitimes.com/News/editorials/archives/2009/07/06/2003447948

Limon, Armando R., 'Misawa to Tear Down Massive "Elephant Cage" Antennae', *Stars and Stripes*, 19 November 2012.

'Local Anger at Japan Island Surveillance Unit', *Aljazeera*, 20 April 2014, at www.aljazeera.com/news/asia-pacific/2014/04/local-anger-at-japan-island-surveillance-unit-201442044145528401.html

Mizokami, Kyle, 'The Mainichi Rides Along with Japan's Senkaku Patrol', *Japan Security Watch*, 17 October 2011, at jsw.newpacificinstitute.org/?p=8524

——, 'Yonaguni is Getting a Garrison', *Japan Security Watch*, 10 November 2010, at jsw.newpacificinstitute.org/?p=3116

'MSDF Admits Losing Submersible in Tsugaru Strait', *Japan Times*, 29 January 2014, at www.japantimes.co.jp/news/2014/01/29/national/msdf-admits-losing-submersible-in-tsugaru-strait/

'MSDF Officer Quizzed Over China Trips: Petty Officer had Classified Information on Foreign Military Vessels at Home', *Yomiuri Shimbun*, 2 August 2006, at www.yomiuri.co.jp/dy/national/20060802TDY02011.htm

'MSDF Tracks China Armada Off Okinawa', *Japan Times*, 14 April 2010, at www.japantimes.co.jp/text/nn20100414a2.html

'MSDF Unmanned Survey Device Lost at Sea after Cable Severed', *Kyodo News International*, 29 January 2014, at www.globalpost.com/dispatch/news/kyodo-news-international/140129/msdf-unmanned-survey-device-lost-at-sea-after-cable-se

'Mystery Sub Sparks Japan Alert', *BBC News*, 10 November 2004, at news.bbc.co.uk/2/hi/3998107.stm

Naoaki Usui, 'Japan Plans to Bolster Already Formidable ASW Ability', *Defense News*, 24 June 1991, p. 14.

'New Scandal Erupts at MSDF', *Asahi Shimbun*, 3 August 2006, at www.asahi.com/english/Herald-asahi/TKY200608030062.html

Nobuhiro Kubo, 'Japan to Arm Remote Western Island, Risking More China Tension', *Reuters*, 18 April 2014, at www.reuters.com/article/2014/04/18/us-japan-military-islands-idUSBREA3H05M20140418

Packler, Martin, 'Japanese Isle in Sea of Contention Weighs Fist Versus Open Hand', *New York Times*, 10 February 2011, at www.nytimes.com/2011/02/11/world/asia/11island.html?pagewanted=all

'Probe Into the Responses Made by the Government to Suspicious Boats', *Asahi Shimbun*, 7 April 1999, in American Embassy, Tokyo, 'Daily Summary of Japanese Press', 12 April 1999, at www.usc.edu/isd/archives/dsjp/summaries/1999/April/Sm990412.doc

'Pro-JGSDF Mayor Wins Reelection', *Weekly Japan Update*, 6 August 2009, at two--plus--two.blogspot.com/2009/08/pro-jsdf-mayor-wins-reelection.html

Ren Zihui, 'Japanese Self-Defense Force Officer Suspected of Divulging Secrets', *Epoch Times*, 4 August 2006, at www.theepochtimes.com/news/6-8-4/44611.html

Ryuji Kudo & Tsukasa Kimura, 'Three Chinese Vessels Pursue Japanese Fishing Boat Near Senkakus', *Asahi Shimbun*, 21 February 2013, at ajw.asahi.com/article/behind_news/social_affairs/AJ201302210082

'SDF Will Build a New Military Base Only 150 km Away from the Diaoyu Islands', 21 June 2013, at www.best-news.us/news-4707397-SDF-will-build-a-new-military-base-is-only-150-km-away-from-the-Diaoyu-Islands.html

'Sea-bottom Cable-laying Ship Operating Offshore: Fishermen Witnessed in About 1972', in 'Report: The Unsinkable Aircraft Carrier Archipelago — Behind the Tomahawk Deployment', *Asahi Shimbun*, 17 June 1984.

'Senkaku/Diaoyu Islands: Japan May Release China Radar Data', *BBC News*, 9 February 2013, at www.bbc.co.uk/news/world-asia-21392248

'Seoul's Spat with Tokyo Boils Over', *Bangkok Post*, 15 July 2008, p. 4.

'Seven Chinese Navy Warships Skirt Okinawa', *Japan Times*, 17 October 2012, at www.japantimes.co.jp/text/nn20121017a3

Sherman, Kenneth B., 'Mystery Sub Detected Off Japanese Coast', *Journal of Electronic Defense* (Vol. 28, No. 1), January 2005, p. 24.

Simpson, James, 'Chinese UAV Spotted by MSDF Aircraft', *Japan Security Watch*, 30 June 2011, at newpacificinstitute.org/jsw/?p=6844

Smith, Charles R., 'Chinese Spy Ships Breach Japanese and Philippine Waters', *NewsMax.Com*, 9 April 2001, at www.newsmax.com/archives/articles/2001/4/8/195441.shtml

'South Korea Survey Angers Japan', *BBC News*, 3 July 2006, at news.bbc.co.uk/2/hi/asia-pacific/5139726.stm

Spitzer, Kirk, 'China Finds a Gap in Japan's Maritime Chokepoints', *Time*, 18 July 2013, at nation.time.com/2013/07/18/china-finds-a-gap-in-japans-maritime-chokepoints/

'Taiwan Boat Seized', *China Post*, 15 September 2009, at www.chinapost.com.tw/taiwan/national/national-news/2009/09/15/224652/Taiwan-boat.htm

'Taiwan Fishing Boat Detained by Japanese Coast Guard', *BBC Monitoring International Reports*, 16 November 2008, at www.encyclopedia.com/doc/1G1-189045422.html

'Taiwan, Japan in High-Seas Standoff', *Taipei Times*, 26 September 2012.

'Talk of the Day: China to Conduct Pacific Naval Drills', *Focus Taiwan*, 24 November 2011, at focustaiwan.tw/ShowNews/WebNews_Detail.aspx?Type=aIPL&ID=201111240049

Taoka Shunji, 'Sea-lane Defence', *Asahi Shimbun*, 1 May 1984.

'The GSDF Deployment to Yonaguni: Making Border Defence Explicit', *Sankei News*, 5 July 2009, at sankei.jp.msn.com/politics/policy/090705/plc0907050128000-n1.htm

'Tokyo Lashes Out About Chinese Ships in Territorial Waters', *Japan Daily Press*, 4 October 2012, at japandailypress.com/tokyo-lashes-out-about-chinese-ships-in-territorial-waters-0414398

'Tokyo Protests Chinese Surveillance Near Islands', *Taipei Times*, 6 February 2007, p. 4.

Tokyo Shimbun, 9 January 1999, in American Embassy, Tokyo, 'Daily Summary of Japanese Press', 13 January 1999.

Trang, Iris, 'China's Navy Floats a Warning to Taiwan', *Asia Times Online*, 25 November 2003, at atimes.com/atimes/China/EK25Ad01.html

'Unidentified Submarine Detected Between Shikoku and Kyushu', *Japan Times*, 15 September 2008.

'Update: China Surveillance Ships Enter Disputed Waters with Japan', *Asahi Shimbun*, 14 September 2012, at ajw.asahi.com/article/behind_news/politics/AJ201209140023

'U.S. and Japan Work Together to Establish Undersea Listening Network Close to Chinese Submarine Bases', *Beijing Daily*, 10 July 2013, at dailynews.sina.com/bg/chn/chnmilitary/sinacn/20130710/00164728365.html

'U.S. Military's "Elephant Cage" Antenna to be Razed', *Japan Times*, 22 November 2012, at www.japantimes.co.jp/news/2012/11/22/national/u-s-militarys-elephant-cage-antenna-to-be-razed/#.Uj_kUX-Kq9J

「走进"中国海监50"号的"心脏"」 ['Walking into the "Heart" of "China Maritime Surveillance 50"'], *Xinhua*, 15 December 2011, at news.xinhuanet.com/mil/2011-12/15/c_122429657.htm

'Yin Zhuo: China Doesn't Need to Inform Japan When Passing Through Miyako Strait', *People's Daily Online*, 12 October 2012, at english.peopledaily.com. cn/90786/7974501.html

'Yonaguni Asks Self Defense Forces for Troop Deployment', *Weekly Japan Update*, 9 July 2009, at two--plus--two.blogspot.com/2009/07/yonaguni-asks-self-defense-forces-for.html

Yuzo Hisatsune, 'Chinese Boats Harass Japanese Fishing Vessels Near Senkakus', *Asahi Shimbun*, 28 February 2013, at ajw.asahi.com/article/asia/china/AJ201302280058

Other electronic sources

'Acoustic Measurement Ship "HIBIKI" Type', *Vessel and Ships Photo Gallery*, at www.vspg.net/jmsdf/aos-hibiki-class.html

'Address by the Hon Alexander Downer MP, at the Third Australia-Japan Conference Dinner', 11 February 2005, at www.foreignminister.gov.au/speeches/2005/050211_3rd_aust_japan_conf.html.

'ADEOS II', Wikipedia, at en.wikipedia.org/wiki/ADEOS_II

'After Taking Office, Koizumi Quietly Expands Japan's Self-Defence Force, Improves Weaponry', 20 May 2003, at japan.people.com.cn/2003/5/21/200352192116.htm

'AGS Nichinan Class', *GlobalSecurity.org*, at www.globalsecurity.org/military/world/japan/nichinan.htm

'AOS Hibiki Class', *GlobalSecurity.org*, at www.globalsecurity.org/military/world/japan/hibiki.htm

'ARC Muroto Class', at www.globalsecurity.org/military/world/japan/muroto.htm

Arthur, Gordon, 'New Anti-Ship Missile for Japan's Self Defence Force', 2 September 2013, at www.shephardmedia.com/news/landwarfareintl/new-anti-ship-missile-japans-self-defence-force/

Batten, Bruce, 'The Founding of Dazaifu', 6 October 2004, at www.fukuokahistory.com/live/content/view/15/52/

Bruel & Kjaer, 'Product Data: Hydrophones — Types 8103, 8104, 8105 and 8106', at www.lthe.fr/LTHE/IMG/pdf/DocBruelKjaerHydro.pdf

Captain Sato, 'Activities of Oceanographic Command JMSDF, 10 February 2012, at www.rioe.or.jp/mts20120210_3.pdf

'Coastal Monitoring Field Training', at www1.linkclub.or.jp/~chi-tan/gozaki.html

'Crisscross Discussion' on 'Officer Being Investigated for Trips to China Found Hanged on MSDF Destroyer in Sasebo', 10 August 2006, at www.crisscross.com/jp/news/381183

'CV: Senior Systems Security Engineer', 11 August 2007, at space-careers.com/agency/cvview_7971.html

'Difference Between SH-60J and SH-60J Kai', at forum.keypublishing.co.uk/archive/index.php?t-47376.html

'ECHELON Station Griesheim with Darmstadt', at hp.kairaven.de/miniwahr/darmstadt-griesheim.html

Fisher, Richard Jr., 'Growing Asymmetries in the China-Japan Naval Balance', 22 November 2005, at www.strategycenter.net/research/pubID.83/pub_detail.asp

'Geography of Japan', Wikipedia, at en.wikipedia.org/wiki/Geography_of_Japan

Herman, Steven L., 'Auxiliarist Reporter/Translator Works to Enhance Relationship with Japan Coast Guard', at www.teamcoastguard.org/2005/May/A050521/japan.htm

Hiroshi Asanuma, Satoshi Hashimoto, Shin-ichi Tano, Sho-ichi Takashima, Mitsutomo Nishizawa, Hiroaki Niitsuma & Yugo Shindo, 'Development of Fiber-optical Microsensors for Geophysical Use', July 2003, at niweb.kankyo.tohoku.ac.jp/PDF/SSC2003_Asanuma.pdf

'Icebreaker Shirase Bids Farewell to Antarctica', 15 February 2007, at www.breitbart.com/print.php?id=D8UR5GE00&show_article=1

'Iki Island', Wikipedia, at wikipedia.org/wiki/Iki_Island

'Iki Patrol Base', at www6.kaiho.mlit.go.jp/fukuoka/kisyou/wakamiya/wakamiya2.htm

'IRSS for Japanese Frigate', Davis Newsletter, July 1997, at www.wrdavis.com/docs/news/html/07/index.html

Isby, David C., 'JGSDF Type 88 Missile Launchers Deployed for Exercise', *IHS Jane's*, 5 November 2013, at www.janes.com/article/29573/jgsdf-type-88-missile-launchers-deployed-for-exercise

'Japanese Fleet', *GlobalSecurity.org*, at www.globalsecurity.org/military/world/japan/jmsdf-orbat.htm

'Japanese Minelayers', at www.battleships-cruisers.co.uk/japanese_minelayers.htm

'Japanese Self-defence Forces to Keep Tabs on East Asia's Seabed', *Alexander's Gas & Oil Connections* (Vol. 9, No. 5), 10 March 2004, at www.gasandoil.com/goc/news/nts41021.htm

'Japan's North Korea War Plan Revealed in a "Novel"', *Shukan Gendai*, 4 April 1988, at www.kimsoft.com/1997/jp-dprk.htm

'Japan's Takeshima X-Files', at dokdo-takeshima.com/dokdo-x-files2.html

'Kawasaki P-1', at www.heinkel.jp/yspack/ysf_p1_eng.html

'Kawasaki P-1 Database ', at harpgamer.com/harpforum/index.php?/topic/17948-kawasaki-p-1/

'Kawasaki P-2J', at p2vneptune.com/v08.shtml

'Kawasaki XP-1 Maritime Patrol Aircraft, Japan', *Naval Technology*, at www.naval-technology.com/projects/kawasaki-xp-1-maritime-patrol-aircraft/

Jet Propulsion Laboratory, 'Mission and Spacecraft Library: MOS 1A, 1B', at space.jpl.nasa.gov/msl/QuickLooks/mosQL.html; and FAO, 'Environmental Satellites', at www.fao.org/docrep/003/t0355e/t0355e05.htm

Masahiko Isobe, 'A Theory of Integrated Coastal Zone Management in Japan', at www.glocom.ac.jp/eco/esena/resource/isobe/index.e.html

'Military Photos and Videos: Japan — Type-88 Surface-to-Ship Missile (SSM-1)', at www.militaryspot.com/gallery/showphoto.php?photo=433&cat=527&page=1

Ministry of Foreign Affairs, Taipei, 'Crew of Sport Fishing Boat Lienhe to Return Home Safely', 19 June 2008, at www.mofa.gov.tw/webapp/ct.asp?xItem=32138&ctNode=761&mp=1

Ministry of the Interior, Taipei, 'Japan Authorities Release Taiwanese Fishing Boat, Crew', 19 November 2008, at www.moi.gov.tw/English/latest_news_detail.aspx?type=taiwan&sn=626

'Naval Security Group Station History Dates', at www.navycthistory.com/ NSGStationsHistoryDates.txt

'N. Korean Spy Ship Shown to Public at Kagoshima Dock', 17 May 2003, at findarticles.com/p/articles/mi_mOXPQ/is_2003_May_20/ai_102043547

Ono Yasumaru, 'Preface to the Chronicle "Kojiki"', at www.geocities.jp/general_ sasaki/oono-yasu-eng.html

'OSIS Ocean Surveillance Information System', *Global Security*, at www. globalsecurity.org/intell/systems/obu.htm

'P2V-7/P-2H', at p2vneptune.com/v07.shtml

'Point of View. Katsutada Kaminuma: Icebreaker Shirase Still Good for Another Year', *Asahi Shimbun*, 11 March 2007, at www.asahi.com/english/Herald-asahi/TKY200711030051.html

'Reviewing ODA or China Policy?: Tokyo Only Expressed Fears', at chinaperspectives.revues.org/document358.html

Saijo Kenji, Ogawara Chiaki, Shimamura Hideki, Sato Ryotaku, Minami Makoto & Tadokoro Yasuaki, 'Optical Fiber Hydrophone Having High Water Pressure Resistance', Patent Number JP2012068087, 5 April 2012, at old.qpat.com/Re nderStaticFirstPage?XPN=TCpRzetWHTd7fYsXyd3avbmsLuw/R4oY%20 QgpgFzVRnM=

Satou Riyoutaku & Koji Dobashi, 'Optical Fiber Hydrophone', Patent Number JP3160092, 16 February 2001, at www.sumobrain.com/patents/jp/Optical-fiber-hydrophone/JP3160092.html

'Scuba Diving: Aomori', *Outdoor Japan*, at www.outdoorjapan.com/activities/ scuba/scuba-diving-ag-aomori.html

'SDF Lost Influence Underwater Robot Submarine Reconnaissance China', 29 January 2014, at www.wantinews.com/news-6326393-SDF-lost-influence-underwater-robot-submarine-reconnaissance-China.html

'Sea Shepherd Being Pursued by Armed Japanese Coast Guard', *Sea Shepherd News*, 30 January 2008, at www.seashepherd.org/news.media_080130_2. html

'Sensors', *America's Navy*, at www.navy.mil/navydata/policy/vision/vis98/ vis-p10.html

'Shonan Class Ocean Survey Ship', *JMSDF Vessels*, at homepage2.nifty.com/ nishidah/e/dtc0635.htm

'Shrimp Aided Submarines: Yankee U-boats Used Snapping Sounds to Foil Jap Detectors', *Reading Eagle*, 16 March 1947, at news.google.com/newspapers?nid=1955&dat=19470316&id=clgrAAAAIBAJ&sjid=-pwFAAAAIBAJ&pg=4836,4206655

'Sikorsky SH-60B "Sea Hawk" 1979', at www.aviastar.org/helicopters_eng/sik_s-70-sea.php

Simpson, James, 'As Plans for Coastal Monitoring Unit Proceed, Yonaguni Residents Raise Voices', 22 August 2011, at jsw.newpacificinstitute.org/?p=7801#comments

——, 'Japan's Ears on the Sea', at medium.com/war-is-boring/japans-ears-on-the-sea-39bf83f0acb7

——, 'Key Figures from the MoD FY2013 Budget Request', *Japan Security Watch*, 7 September 2012, at jsw.newpacificinstitute.org/?p=10480

'Sound Surveillance System (SOSUS)', Discovery of Sound in the Sea (DOSITS), at www.dosits.org/gallery/tech/pt/sosus1.htm

Spiegel, Young, 'U.S. Listening Stations at Misawa Designed to Uncover Russian and DPRK Military Secrets', at www.globalview.cn/ReadNews.asp?NewsID=30553

'SSM-1: Shibasuta SSM-1B Type 88, Type 90', at www.deagel.com/Anti-Ship-Missiles/SSM-1_a001943001.aspx

Stark, Ronald F., 'A Diving Instructor's Journal: 2001 Adventures', 15 November 2001, at www.heronet.ne.jp/~rfstark/Log2001.htm

——, 'Divine Wind Adventures: Dive Report 20 June 2009', at www.divinewindadventures.com/frame contents.htm

——, 'Scuba Diving Sites: Popular Locations in the Aomori Prefecture', at divinewindadventures.com/Dive-Sites.htm

'Tappizaki Diving of the Tsugaru Peninsula', at www.japanguides.net/aomori/tappizaki-diving-of-the-tsugaru-peninsula.html

'The Truth About Misawa: The Ping-pong Balls Which Multiply', 2 May 2000, at www.toonippo.co.jp/rensai/ren2000/misawa/msw0502.html

Toppan, Andrew, 'World Navies Today: Japan', 23 May 2002, at www.hazegray.org/worldnav/asiapac/japan.htm

'Wokou', Wikipedia, at en.wikipedia.org/wiki/Wokou

Zeni Lite Buoy Company, 'Company Events, Fiscal Year 1993', at www.zenilite. co.jp/topics/p14.html

Made in the USA
San Bernardino, CA
06 March 2016